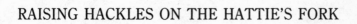

RAISING HACKLES ON THE HATTIE'S FORK

RAISING HACKLES ON THE HATTIE'S FORK

And other tales of mishaps and misdeeds while fishing and hunting in the North Woods

KENT COWGILL

THE ATLANTIC MONTHLY PRESS
NEW YORK

Published simultaneously in Canada
Printed in the United States of America

FIRST EDITION

Library of Congress Cataloging-in-Publication Data

Cowgill, Kent.
Raising hackles on the Hattie's Fork: and other tales of mishaps and misdeeds while fishing and hunting in the North Woods / Kent Cowgill.—1st ed.
ISBN 0-87113-292-3
1. Hunting. 2. Fishing. I. Title.
SK33.C668   1991   799—dc20   90-887

Design by Laura Hough

The Atlantic Monthly Press
19 Union Square West
New York, NY 10003

FIRST PRINTING

Out of the woods,
with love and appreciation,
for Erich and Andrew

Contents

CONTENTS

CONTENTS

Preface

ASK ANY NATIVE MIDWESTERNER AND IT'S ALMOST
certain he'll remember the moment when an outsider, usually
someone from the East, cracked the chrysalis of his regional
insularity. It typically happens in late adolescence. Since I grew
up in rural Nebraska, as sheltered a cloister as remains any-
where in this country, my own rite of passage was delayed until
my first year of graduate school.

Hustling across campus one fall Saturday afternoon with
hundreds of other high-spirited zealots toward yet another
Cornhusker bloodletting, I found myself suddenly face to face
with a recent seminar acquaintance who had somehow made his
way to the University of Nebraska from the Bronx. Though no
older than I, he was balding, jowly, and bearded. His eyebrows
beetled behind wire-rimmed glasses; his world-weary shoulders

PREFACE

slouched. From his right paw hung a ratty leather briefcase bulging with arcane tomes from the library.

We stood for a moment in awkward silence on the sidewalk as the red-clad stream parted around us and then flowed on toward Memorial Stadium.

"What do people in the East think about all this?" I asked.

His answer, as predictable as it was immediate, landed flush in my prairie ingenuousness:

"They don't."

It wasn't until I'd left the Midwest and spent some time on both coasts that I understood why they don't. And it wasn't until I'd reached middle age, by then a transplanted Minnesotan with a considerably more seasoned perspective on cultural cocooning, that I gradually began to feel they should.

In retrospect, I see that this book began with that dawning awareness that the American heartland had some things to offer besides clean air, corn, and good football. One of those things is a largely unspoken but impassioned love affair with the outdoors.

Whose woods they are I think I know. With an obligatory nod toward Frost, I think that after two decades of roaming the trout streams and grouse coverts of my adopted North Woods I know them as he knew their more pastoral counterparts in New England. Mine are inhabited by the rogues' gallery of quietly crazed fishermen and hunters who appear in the pages that follow.

I remain insular enough to like nearly every one of them— despite, or maybe because of, their want of urban polish. Which is not to claim for them any distinctive qualities unshared by their sporting brethren elsewhere. Local color aside, non-Midwestern readers of this book will doubtless find our differences to be less in kind than in the degree of our sporting obsessions.

PREFACE

Terminal cases crop up everywhere, from Maui to Manhattan; there are simply more of us in the Midwest.

To the evidence offered by the following twenty stories I'll add the testimony of my brother, a cardiovascular surgeon in Wisconsin. He swears that every November he has patients in serious need of heart bypass operations who postpone them until after deer-hunting season has closed. It's not an anecdote I pass along to locals. My guess is that most of them would react only by raising their eyebrows slightly in anticipation of the punch line.

RAISING HACKLES ON THE HATTIE'S FORK

Raising Hackles on the Hattie's Fork

THE PICKUP SKIDDED TO A CLANKING STOP JUST short of the bridge abutment, loose gravel peppering the metal railings like birdshot. Even from where I stood some fifty yards downstream, I could tell the fellow was unfriendly. Ignoring the well-worn path, he bulled headlong through waist-high nettles, hitched up his bib overalls at the crotch, and stiffly jacked one leg over the fence. Still straddling the barbed wire, he paused long enough to jet a stream of tobacco juice across the stile our chapter had installed a few hours earlier, then charged downhill toward the bend where I was working.

"You the fella with them Trout Unlimited stickers all over your car?" he challenged.

Readily acknowledging the fact, I hammered home the final nail in the underwater crib I had been constructing. Perfectly positioned at the angle of an elbow pool, it would hold trout for years to come.

"What the devil you doin' to the crick?" he bellowed.

The chance to educate the unenlightened comes rarely to any angler, and I sprang at the opportunity. Our latest chapter project, I noted proudly, was "Habitat on the Hattie's Fork: An Alarum for Anglers," and the crib shelter I had just finished was only part of the stream's continuing reclamation.

"I'll be damned," he cackled. "So it ain't a rabbit hutch. Sure obliged you told me it's a hidy-hole for trout, seein' how it ain't gonna be there after the first good rain what washes down from them foothills."

I gestured toward the stout anchoring posts implanted in the streambed, but this seemed only to provoke him. Laughter gurgled in his throat like rusty water in a desert well.

Hoping to direct his attention elsewhere, I pointed downstream. Where a few days earlier a half-drowned auto body clogged the sluggish current, swift water now burbled over a bed of rocks we'd trucked in from a nearby quarry. It was a metamorphosis even such a man as he couldn't help but appreciate.

Instead, he staggered backward as if stricken, a look of horror spreading across his stubbled face. "Judas Priest!" he bellowed. "What in the hell have you gone and done to the Edsel Pool?"

He then lurched downstream toward the work, I trailing behind him, fearful he would somehow try to disfigure it even though it comprised some sixty-odd tons of dolomite. When I overtook him, however, he seemed strangely subdued. Eyes glazed, he stood at the pool's edge with the water lapping at his overshoe buckles, his voice scarcely audible, his jaw slack. Rarely have I seen a man look more dispirited.

"Gone . . . it's all gone," he whispered. "One of the best

gawdammed holes in the country, and you boys have up and ruined it. Ain't been but a month ago I sat here and took my limit on nightcrawlers right out from under the left headlight, and now there ain't nothin' left. The Edsel Pool! We had a stretch o' water here even Ted's Trout Haven would of been proud of, and you boys have gone and tore it all to hell."

His shoulders sagged as he turned and shambled off down-stream to where we had replaced another unsightly heap of debris with transplanted beds of watercress. Even as we watched, a trout rose regularly to a *Caenis* hatch in the narrowed channel.

"And look what you went and done to Hotpoint Hole," he groaned. "One of the best places on God's green earth to still-fish with Velveeta or marshmallows, and you've clogged it all up with a big ol' crapload of moss. Used to be almost as good here as down at Deadbolt Corner, and now what's left? Nothin' but a little trickle what sounds like a cow piddlin' on a flat rock."

"But the fish are there," I responded. "Take the rise we just. . . ."

"And what kind of fish are we talkin'?" he shot back, arching a stream of tobacco juice past my neoprene waders. "Little bitty cigars what could barely get their mouths around a hook-sized chunk of sucker belly. Shootfire, boy, let's talk *trout,* not minnies. Where are your hawgs gonna live? You've took out ever' last washin' machine and tractor tire in the crick!"

"Faulty logic!" I countered. "Our post-project electro-shocking shows increased poundage per water-acre. You simply can't see the fish now because of the improved habitat. Even so, I'd wager that if later this evening you were to lay a Humpy under that shoreline willow, or perhaps twitch a wiggle nymph in the shadows alongside those . . ."

"Great Gawdamighty!" he roared. "You fellas *are* preverts,

just like Roach Schollmeier said. I should of knowed it from the beginning. It ain't enough that you're all on dope—always talkin' about 'shootin' heads' and how good the 'goofus bug's' been workin' for you lately. You're preverts to boot!"

It was such a ludicrous misconception I became quite exercised in attempting to correct it, but he remained so aroused I might as well have been speaking to a post.

"Yessirree, it all commences to make sense to me now. Drugs and sex and God only knows what else goin' on down here on the Hattie's Fork ever evenin'! I knowed a long time ago you boys didn't give a hoot about breakin' the law—always braggin' about how easy it is to make the 'double haul'—but I just figured, what the hell, there's plenty of fish for ever'body. Shootfire, once or twice I've come down here at midnight with a can of kernel corn and made the old double haul myself. And even when I heard some of you talkin' about Ratface McDougal and the Woolly Bugger I just said to myself, 'Now be honest, Virgil, some of the fellas you fish with wouldn't exactly fit into the church choir on Sunday mornin', neither.'

"But goldang it, boy, that bunch of yours ain't just makin' a little hanky-panky down here on the crick bank, we're talkin' out-and-out corruption. And what's really the topper, you don't even appear to see nothin' wrong with it! Just last week, for instance, I heard one of you carryin' on about his 'new vice.' Then the guy he was talkin' to pipes up and says, 'I know exactly what you mean, Clancy. Until I found a good vise I never could get a really tight wrap with Polly Dubbing.'

"After that he kept on like some drunken sailor and said he wanted to show him his old Irresistible, what worked so well 'when he needed to attract her.' I'm here to tell you, I was hoppin' mad. It's bad enough a man his age would take up with some little gal that's probly young enough to be his daughter, but to stand there and tell another fella all about it, braggin' about how much he loved spinnin' and clippin' those dear body hairs, why I knowed right away it was all a bunch of preversions. Specially when he complained about never havin' enough room to really whip finish her good!

"And just think about that little Polly Dubbing. I bet she can't hardly show her face for shame.

"But you think even that would faze them two boys? Hell, no! They just went on and on, sayin' how when they couldn't get a rise out of 'em it sometimes worked to just tease 'em a little with the ole grizzly king.

"I'm here to tell you, they finally got me so mad I jumped up off my bucket—trippin' over my stringer in the process—and chased both them boys downriver 'till I couldn't run no more. Alls I could do at the end was throw stuff. But that just might of been enough. I'll guarantee you for sure I caught one of 'em flush in the ass with a five-ounce sinker, and I nailed the other one in the leg with a lard can full of chicken guts. It was worth it too, even if I did lose all my bait and couldn't fish no more."

When at last he paused for breath, I seized the initiative, attempting as best I could to explain to him the ancient art of angling with the fly. Unfortunately, not having at hand my fly rod with which properly to demonstrate, I was forced to mime for him such subtleties as the double haul and the roll cast, all of which I performed with that broad exaggeration so necessary when educating a novice as unschooled as he.

Throughout my demonstration he stood with mouth agape, his body tense and mistrustful, as if I were about to snatch away his wallet or spring forward and do him bodily harm.

I had just started to expound on the countless rewards of

fly-tying, summarizing a short list of basic tying materials he would need in order to begin, when he babbled something incoherent, edged away, and began to run.

"Jungle cock," I continued, trotting after him. "Latex rubber sheets."

Staggering, he tripped over a mud-encrusted bed frame we'd dredged from the stream, but somehow righted himself and stumbled on.

"Pocket gopher guard hairs," I shouted more loudly. "Starling rump feathers. Mottled turkey shorts!"

By now he was approaching the road, his shirttail flapping from his overalls and his arms swinging wildly akimbo.

"Urine-stained vixen belly!"

With a muffled groan he leaped toward the ditch, barely clearing the top strand of barbed wire, and disappeared into the nettles. Concerned that he might have injured himself, I too began to sprint. Before I could help him, however, he regained his feet and scrambled up to his pickup. I stood watching at the fence as he careened away up the road.

Had I done something untoward to provoke such eccentric behavior? Was there even yet the possibility he might some day see the light?

I don't know. Somehow it never fails to depress me, encountering a man whom it's impossible to educate.

Anglers of Vision

IT'S A CURIOUS THING, HOW PEOPLE THAT DON'T FISH feel about fishermen. Not disrespect, exactly, and nothing close to the hide-the-kids hysteria reserved for the man who confesses to enjoying the occasional trip afield with a gun. What it is, I think most anglers would tell you, is some combination of awkwardness, bemusement, and pity, akin to the way one feels about a ne'er-do-well uncle who comes to Sunday dinner and spills gravy on his pants.

What we're talking about here is a public perception so deeply rooted that a twinge of inferiority eventually sprouts in many a fisherman's psyche. A glance at English usage exposes the antifisherman bias for all to see. Try to remember, for example, the last time you heard the word "fish" used with positive connotations. Now consider how often the opposite is the case. A shady deal is fishy. A coarse woman is a fishwife. A fish story is a baldfaced lie. Socially, you're a fish out of water if you smell like a fisherman even if you're adept at fishing for compliments—unless you're so bad a poker player you're everybody's favorite fish.

Where the English language is concerned, even hunters come off better than fishermen, as the pundits of electoral politics remind us every four years. A longshot who does some early bird-dogging in Iowa, bagging enough votes to head on to New Hampshire still in the hunt for delegates, has got a real shot at going after bigger game in the fall. If people think he's feeding them a line, on the other hand, he'll most likely face a backlash, especially if voters swallow opposition charges that his party is short on moral leadership—rotting, like a fish, from the head down.

Film images of the fisherman also pale in comparison with the silver screen's legions of virile gun-toters, as Henry Fonda's doddering "old poop" adrift on Golden Pond attests. If you take your fishing seriously, it's easy to become a little paranoid about such cinematic ego-bashing. Was one of the All-American golden boys of the 1950s dubbed Tab Hunter simply by accident, for example, in an era when Eddie Fisher came off as the feckless fall guy, chronic loser at the game of love?

What's particularly depressing in all this is what it says about the decline of Western Civilization. For the truth is, fishermen got off to a damned good start. Both Jonah and the apostle Peter were fishermen. So were Andrew, James, and John. Even Jesus liked to get out on the water occasionally. And who could ask for more support than the charge to go forth and become fishers of men?

It's been all downhill since. Unless I'm missing somebody,

for the next nineteen centuries the only fishermen of any real repute are Captain Ahab and Izaak Walton: a monomaniac and a guy who couldn't spell.

In the twentieth century things have gotten even worse. Part of the problem is that fishing has managed to get itself tagged "The Sport of Presidents," a label that hangs like an albatross around every fisherman's neck. The mental imagery the phrase conjures up is the heaviest burden: Calvin Coolidge, in stiff collar and face, holding what is either a stringered trout or a short umbrella; Herbert Hoover looking depressed on the Housatonic; Jimmy Carter backpedaling in a bass boat, fighting off an attacking rabbit with an oar. True, Eisenhower seems to have taken a fish or two in his time, and George Bush has plunged belly deep into the fight against angling wimphood. Some might even take as a good omen Marlin Fitzwater's prominence among the Bushmen. But as a historical hook to hang your ego on, such minutiae don't offer much consolation. Especially if you're a Democrat.

It's time for a change, time to upgrade our collective image. I'm not suggesting anything radical here. No formation of a Fishermen's Liberation Front (FLF), though this is what a carp-fishing friend of mine thinks it's going to take. What I have in mind is nothing more than *honesty,* a kind of Anglish counter-attack, an attempt to show the uninformed what it's really like out there on America's rivers and lakes.

In a few areas, admittedly, there's not much we can do to change the public bias. It's tough to look sexy in a belly boat, and you're not going to come off as cerebral tossing a Fuzz-E-Grub with an Ugly Stik. It's also pointless to point to the bulldog determination of the average bullhead fisherman. No matter how you package him, he's still going to look like Gomer Pyle.

Such obstacles notwithstanding, we can do a lot to improve

our public posture. A logical place to start is with the three stereotypes people that don't fish seem to have formed—God only knows how—about fishermen. Depending on where you fish and what you fish for, the three typically break down along these lines:

1. *Fishermen are lazy.* A panfisherman usually serves as the benchmark here, a drawling rustic who plops down on a bait bucket and dangles a worm through heavy clots of duckweed, there to vegetate for hours, moving only when his bobber gives a torpid twitch.

2. *Fishermen are shallow.* The prototype here is the bass fisherman in a boat, considered shallow no matter how deep the lake he's fishing. Throw in a six-pack of beer and he's one happy sum'bitch, even if the bass aren't hitting, 'specially if there's a purty woman singin' on the raidyo.

3. *Fishermen are pretentious.* This one is the trickiest by far, and almost always reserved for dry fly fishermen, those "pointy-headed intellectuals" who dress like Oxford dons and pontificate in Latin on the mating habits of mayflies, usually with briar pipes in their mouths.

How people have come to form such cockeyed opinions is anybody's guess. What's important is correcting them. That is easier said than done, unfortunately, given fishermen's habitual reserve. Consider further how reflexive among fishermen is that distrust of outsiders bred by two millennia of being patronized—a kind of English xenophobia—and even such an apparently simple matter as "telling people what it's really like" gets thorny as hell.

What follows is one man's attempt to come out of the

closet, some straight talk about public ignorance by a fisherman unique only in his willingness to tell the truth about *fishing talk*—the things fishermen say to one another. Nothing more than this frank disclosure of on-the-water discourse should be necessary to counter public misperceptions. Nothing less will do the job.

Taking the negative stereotypes one by one, then, here are the facts:

1. So far are fishermen from being "lazy" that their speech is larded with signs of energy and resolution: "What have you *tried?*" "Is anything *working?*" "I've *run through* every damned thing in my box!" to cite only a few. Any backsliding toward sloth is met with rigorous moral censure, evident in such rebukes as "Slow action, too much play" and the oft-heard "Take up the slack!"

So deep-seated is this commitment to the work ethic that most fishermen eventually become dedicated philanthropists, ever willing to help those in need. It would be no exaggeration to consider them outright Platonists, their inner eye fixed unblinkingly on the Good. Even the lowly bullhead fisherman serves to make this widely underpublicized fact clear. Approaching another of his kind on the banks of a muddy farm pond, for example, the bullheader will, almost invariably, first ask, "Doing any Good?"

While rejoinders to this genteel query are varied, "Just getting started" is probably the most common, a taciturn disclosure that says as much about the average angler's modesty as it does about his commitment to the Platonic Ideal. I know fishermen so humble that "Just getting started" is what they'll respond no matter how many hours of unrewarded labor they've put in.

2. The second stereotype—that fishermen are shallow—is an equally myopic distortion. For argument's sake, let's grant that our ranks do include a few beer-swilling water-bangers who probably won't make it to more than one or two Impressionist exhibitions in their lifetimes. Let's even grant that the public's image of the prototype, the bass fisherman in a boat, is of a man a tad less likely to enjoy Mozart than he does Johnny Paycheck. So what? The truth is, beneath this redneck facade lie men of genuine substance, and none are more genuinely substantial than the weighty folk who fish for bass.

Their relentless quest for *structure* is the best evidence of this fact. Indeed, even a relatively inexperienced bass fisherman is almost certain to show profound commitment to the search. "Not enough structure" is the chronic lament of these water-borne depth-finders, who might fairly be called the structuralists of outdoor life. At their most analytical, such boat-seat Platonists probe Nature's secrets to levels beyond the capacity of language to communicate, a shadowy world of forms expressible only in the arcane numerology of Pythagorean math. On those rare occasions when they do speak—often hunched over hydrographic maps marked with sinuous lines and cryptic clusters of X's—they generally do so in algebraic equations indecipherable to the layman. "Where are the *points?*" is a recurrent theme. So also is "pattern," as in "Now what the hell kind of pattern you figure they're in?"

It's a hard life, meditative, misunderstood, largely unrewarded. For this reason, the bassmaster is often the most solitary of men.

3. The third stereotype—the fly fisherman as pretentious egghead—is obviously at odds with the two we've just considered. In figurative terms, the angling Anglophile is to the bassin' or bullhead man what pâté on French bread is to crackers and cheese.

Of all the stereotypes this one is by far the trickiest to counter, and not because it bears any relationship to the truth. In fact, fly fishermen are as a rule uncommonly pragmatic and level-headed. As naturalists, they have no other choice. The problem is that, to people who don't fish, their appearance, language, and equipment convey the opposite impression. To the nonfisherman, such basic research tools as the trout stomach pump and the stream thermometer work to reinforce the stereotype, as does even such practical apparel as the multipocket vest. Sadly, these are only a few obvious instances of neglect. Any serious fly fisherman could cite dozens of others.

The tragedy of such stereotyping is the public ignorance it nurtures, ignorance especially of recent efforts to harness the vast untapped labor potential of trout. Most nonfishermen seem at least faintly familiar with the trout's relative intelligence, and a few may even be aware of Swisher and Richards's investigations into the fish's ability to understand Latin and Greek. I've yet to meet a single nonangler, however, who knows anything about the Streamside Observation Behaviorists, perhaps because so little glamour attaches to piscatorial motor research.

It's a shame, for nobody fortunate enough to know a dedicated SOB could ever again think of fishermen as "pointy-headed." Indeed, so successful have been their recent experiments that some Streamside Observation Behaviorists privately predict trout will eventually be trained to perform most of America's menial labor. I say *"privately predict"* because in public the SOBs are cautious to a fault. Away from the stream, they may be even more close-mouthed than the Structuralists.

Yet *on* the stream, conducting their experiments in trout-labor training, they're among the most vocal and excitable of men, punctuating their triumphs with euphoric cries of "There's a fish working!" or "You've really got the bastard laboring now!" In truth, nothing moves an SOB to full-throated passion like the sight of a large trout working. And nothing depresses him like those enigmatic days when the fish refuse to work at all. Much research remains to be done, he'll tell you then, on ways to increase their productivity.

Getting fish to work up to their capacity, of course, has long been a problem in America, and it isn't likely we're soon going to see any dramatic change. The SOBs to a man warn us of this hard fact. It will take cutthroat competition—and rainbows and browns as well—to meet the stiffening foreign challenge. The word is, nothing works like a Japanese trout.

The Wager

OLD ORVAL LINDQUIST HAD BEEN THE FIRST TO HOOK him. In a humid August nightfall with cicadas droning in the elms, he had fought the fish he couldn't see through the darkening shadows, the heavy rod clenched in his arthritic hands, his nerves fraying like the braided silk line that had finally snapped. By eight-thirty the next morning he sat in Muller's Feedstore, his bent fingers so stiff he could barely hold a coffee cup, battling now just as futilely against the mocking disbelief of his peers.

"Well he was that big anyway, I don't give a good goddamn what you fellas say."

"Tell us again," Shump Jumbeck prodded. "Just how big are we talkin'? I think we got it down to somewhere between a side of beef and a chain saw."

Aside from Donk Muller, the proprietor, who doubled as

village clerk and notary public, there was no one in the store but Jumbeck and Harley Shepard. Slouched on sacks of feed by the door, they had finally goaded the old man into uncustomary peevishness. Coffee sloshed from his cup as he slapped the side of his chair in irritation, spotting the grain-dusted floor.

"I told you pea-brains this ain't no fish story. I never saw him! Alls he did was move back and forth, always stayin' deep, just workin' that pool like a combine in an oats field. Never any faster, never any slower. He just kept on moving up and back, up and back—like a *reaper.*"

The Cronies had laughed until tears came to their eyes. But when the old man had returned to the pool that evening at sunset, his new reel freshly wound with high-test monofilament, he found two cars parked along the township road a hundred yards away.

Within a week every fisherman in the village knew the hole where the big brown lived. Two miles below Frieburg, Crooked Creek funneled into a trough pool no wider than a heron's wingspan, chest deep and gun-metal blue. Locals called it The Narrows. It was the last good stretch of water before the creek turned sluggish above the Mississippi—snail-paced, mud-bottomed, choked with willows—like a hard-bodied boxer gone to paunch and jowl overnight.

It wasn't until the following spring that the old farmer's story was verified. On the first warm weekend in May a stranger from Minneapolis, a college professor, had appeared in the Frieburg post office to inquire about "angling prospects in the area." He was directed at once to the feedstore. As always on Saturday morning, a half-dozen locals lounged in varying states of wakefulness on bulging sacks of feed and fertilizer. When the door creaked open, their heads turned slowly toward it.

The Professor was short and ruddy, bullnecked, with an

impeccably trimmed white beard—Henry VIII outfitted by L. L. Bean. The florid face was overhung by a mesh sun helmet, and he wore tan safari trousers and a matching chamois shirt. A silver assortment of clips, rings, and scissors dangled from his unsoiled fly vest like a dowager's jewelry.

"Gawddog," one of the Cronies murmured.

Eyeing one another like pipefitters listening to the spiel of a politician in a hardhat, they sat stone-faced as the Professor made his address. When he finished, Shump Jumbeck pulled a rumpled handkerchief from the hip pocket of his jeans, shook it out, and blew his nose. "Let me see if I got any of this straight," he said. "You lost me somewhere between that big beaver kill back East and the time over in England when you spent a week testin' your itchin'. Near as I can tell, what it all comes down to is you're after a hawg."

"A what?"

"A hawg. A big'un. A fish so bodacious you'd need the bed of a pickup truck to haul him home."

"Not at all. In point of fact, I'm simply sated with small trout from stocked streams. I thought that perhaps down here in the . . . down here where there aren't so many anglers, I might find something more akin to those waters especially hospitable to large browns."

"Well sir, let me be the first to tell you Frieburg's a far cry from hawg heaven. It ain't like our fish think a hook is a hunch-backed worm. Any more it seems like ever'time I get out on Crooked Crick, there sets old Harley Shepard"—and with a sidelong glance at the offender he stuffed his left cheek with a chaw of Copenhagen—"there's old Harley sleepin' in the sun with his rod propped in the crotch of a cut willow. Like I say, it just ain't that easy here. A fifteen-incher means braggin' rights for a week."

"Then I've been badly misinformed. A fellow in the post office told me you have a wonderfully large trout somewhere nearby."

At that, like sidetracked freight cars jerked slowly into motion, the Cronies began to stir. Harley Shepard, his lanky frame draped across half a dozen feedsacks, was the first to respond.

"I guess you must be talkin' about the Reaper, the big brown that lives in the Narrows down below town? Big as a pup Lab, ever'body says, though personally I ain't never seen him."

"I'm not certain. Your postmaster didn't seem too well apprised."

Rubbing his stubbled chin, Shump Jumbeck nodded at Ralph McCrary. "Say Ralph, didn't you have a crack at the Reaper just a week or so ago?"

"Yessir, indeed I did. Nearly landed him too, but my old lady moves about as fast as a wing-tipped duck. He was gone by the time she managed to get the net ready. Must've been ten, maybe twelve pounds. Biggest brown I ever saw in my life."

Barely hesitating, the Professor took the bait and ran. "Truly now? A trout that large in Crooked Creek? Would you gentlemen mind divulging where I might have a go at him?"

At that the general overseer of the daily feedstore bull-swap, Donk Muller, eased out from behind the counter. He was almost exactly the same height and weight as the Professor, and fully as imposing in his baggy bib overalls, except that in the halls of academe his domain would not have been the lecture room but the heating plant.

Snapping the tip of a wooden match with a single gnarled thumbnail, he lit the store's propane burner, nursed the flame to life, and set the store's dinged coffee pot down with a heavy metallic clank. Chores finished, he finally turned and spoke.

"Friend, I gather you *are* talkin' about the Reaper, and the Reaper never leaves The Narrows down in Hank Wentersdorf's hayfield. These fellas here have tried ever' way they know to hook him, one way or another, though you ain't likely to get none of 'em to admit it. The fact is, nobody's ever even seen that fish."

Satisfied he'd finally found a single honest man among a horde of barbarians, the Professor got his directions to the pool.

Two hours later he was back in the feedstore, his chest heaving, his waders wet to the waist. No one remained except Donk and Harley Shepard, who dozed by the door.

"I hooked him!"

Donk shut his account book. "You what?"

"I hooked him. He's there, just as you said. I tried dry flies, then nymphs, then a varied assortment of streamers, but I couldn't move him. Finally, on a whim, I drifted an orange salmon fly deep, and he took. Only once did I actually catch a glimpse of him, big and dark in the water, moving up and back along the shoreline. In the end he simply carried on downstream into an underwater brushpile, where he snapped my tippet like gossamer."

From that day, the Reaper lived. It wasn't long before the fish was a household word in the valley, even to those who had never set foot in Crooked Creek, and within the year he was known throughout Wabasha County.

Occasionally, among the fishermen who appeared in the feedstore to announce that they had hooked him, there came someone who actually had: the local implement dealer, jigging a bottom-sunk gob of redworms after a thunderstorm had turned the water to chocolate; a Mississippi riverman who hooked him on a sun-dried chunk of pork; a twelve-year-old girl drift-fishing a piece of cheese under a bobber. But he escaped them all.

Nobody had ever really seen the fish, except as a ghost sliding by in the shoreline shadows. But the accounts were invariably the same. Up and back, bull-strong, relentlessly hugging the bottom, until in fatigue or boredom he finally powered on downstream and sheared off the line.

He was simply the Reaper, cutting his swath.

From the day he had hooked the fish and lost him to the autumn Friday when he again walked into the feedstore—over a year later—the Professor had not been seen in Frieburg. Yet he addressed the assembly of Cronies as if back from a short afternoon nap.

"Gentlemen, I have a wager to propose. Tomorrow morning I shall not only hook, but land, the Reaper. And I am prepared to venture a hundred dollars on it, taking odds of ten to one."

For several seconds the Cronies were speechless, slackjawed in disbelief. Perched behind the counter on his overstuffed barstool, Donk Muller pulled a tin of tobacco from his pocket and extracted a hefty chaw. "What'sat agin?" he mumbled. His cheek bulging, he eyed the Professor like a suspicious fat squirrel on a stump.

"I'm wagering I can catch the Reaper. He's still down there, isn't he? Tomorrow morning. Ten to one."

With that the Cronies erupted in chorus, "You're on!" . . . "I'll take that bet!" . . . "Get it on paper!"—slapping their thighs and cackling with unrestrained glee.

Sliding off his stool, Donk waddled back to the squat iron safe and ceremoniously dialed the combination. The door swung open heavily, revealing a stack of account books, canceled checks, and thin piles of cash. He removed a brown-spined ledger and lugged it back to the linoleum counter top.

The Wager

"All right, I'm damned sure I speak for ever'body in here. We'll take that bet, at two hundred fifty bucks a head." Looking around at the others and hearing no dissent, he unsheathed a black fountain pen and proceeded to write with the painstaking care of a nearsighted accountant: "Agreed on Sept. 25, 1988, before the witnesses below signatured"—and he handed the pen to the four Cronies who earnestly scrawled their names above his own—"that if I land the trout known as the Reaper, in The Narrows, between sunrise and sunset on Saturday, Sept. 28, I will be imbursed the sum of $1,000. If I fail to land him, I will forfeiture to the beforesigned the sum of $100, to be equally departed between them."

When the Professor unhesitatingly reached for the pen, Shump Jumbeck led a round of back-slapping that continued off and on until Donk closed the store at suppertime.

By six-thirty the next morning, as the first rays of sun cleared the maples on the ridgetops, so many cars were parked below the town that it appeared a farm auction was about to begin. If the official population of the village was 232, nearly all Frieburg stood in the autumn chill alongside the highway, drowsily drinking coffee and rubbing their hands to keep warm.

The Professor did not appear until seven. Parking his car at the end of the line, he assembled his rod as if tuning a Stradivarius, cinched up his waders, and stepped gingerly across the sagging barbed-wire fence. Stirred by his appearance, the crowd dropped their cups to scramble after him through the damp meadow grass. He strode on toward the streambank as if unaware of their presence, but once there, he turned abruptly and spoke.

"Please pay heed, good people. A fly in the eye is not a pleasant experience. Make whatever noise you wish but allow me sufficient space to cast."

Chastened only momentarily, the crowd inched forward as the angler tied on what appeared to be a large hank of orange yarn. When a few of the locals began to giggle, it was all the inspiration Shump Jumbeck required.

"Don't forget," he said loudly, "We ain't down here to watch you knit a sweater." Laughter swelled for a full minute as the jest passed backward through the streamside throng. Ignoring the commotion, the Professor eased into the water and began to work the rod until forty feet of fly line unfurled effortlessly in tight looping coils behind him, the weighted fly finally splashing down into the riffle just above the pool.

The strike was anticlimactic, too sudden to be believed. But it became clear after no more than a few seconds that a big fish was on. And when the pearl fly line began moving steadily back and forth through The Narrows, bending the rod almost double, a single voice rose in tribute from the stunned crowd along shore. It was Donk Muller, whose words hung over the multitude like a collective affirmation:

"Lord love a goose."

As the fish held doggedly for several minutes to its circling course up and down the pool, the Professor was pressed for an explanation. Finally he consented. For two days he had come to The Narrows at daybreak, crouching low in the grass above the riffle, only to toss clusters of salmon eggs into the water. At dawn on the previous morning, finally satisfied with the Reaper's education, he had threaded on a hookless egg cluster and given the fish his final exam. When the strike came at once, he had gently pulled free, cased his rod, and headed straight for Muller's Feedstore.

Granted front-row status because of their personal stake in the proceedings, the Cronies stood goggle-eyed along the bank. With the conviction of a shell-shocked quarterback who has thrown a string of interceptions, Shump Jumbeck croaked, "It ain't right. You chummed him, and that ain't fair."

Mesmerized by the line severing the water, no one responded.

The fish continued to circle. Once, rod tip held high, the Professor reached for his net as if the moment of truth was imminent, then laughed aloud as the fish powered back upstream into the pool.

"Fight on," he cried. "Fight on, brave old fellow."

The escape run came a few minutes later. As if jolted by an electric current, the fish moved out of The Narrows and surged. Through the gauntlet of bystanders it drove downstream toward freedom, the Professor floundering behind in thigh-deep water, the crowd bobbing along shore like flotsam trailing in the wake.

Then just as suddenly, around the bend, the frenzied action abruptly stopped. Standing stock still in the sluggish current above the snag that had undone all challengers before him, the Professor gasped triumphantly for breath. Thickly sheathed in a bedsheet, the snag's tangle of underwater roots had been rendered as harmless as a wasp in amber. Stymied, the fish held for half a minute beneath a mud bank along the opposite shore, then headed slowly back upstream.

"It ain't right!" Shump Jumbeck shouted. "You sealed him off." But it was Donk Muller who spoke for the rest. "City man, if you get him in, as far as I'm concerned you've earned him. I'd give my two fifty just for one good look at that old sonofabuck."

Back and forth cut the Reaper through The Narrows, the line shearing like a sickle, the runs shorter and shallower until at last the torpedo body loomed just below the surface film. Their eyes riveted on the fish, the Cronies leaned so far forward it appeared they would topple into the water.

The crowd stilled as the Professor raised the rod tip and reached for his net, a congregation silenced by the upraised hand of a priest. For a prolonged moment the only sound was the line's silky hissing.

Then suddenly the net swooped deep, and the fish was swept toward the sky, a great golden fish throwing spray and thrashing violently, while the Professor sounded a euphoric yawp that echoed triumphantly from ridge to ridge. As it died away, nothing moved but the fish still quivering in the mesh.

It was Donk Muller who finally broke the silence.

"That ain't a trout," he said.

The Professor lowered his head and opened his eyes.

"What do you mean? It's the Reaper—no question about it."

"Mebbe so, but it sure as hell ain't no trout."

The Professor looked at Donk, then down at the net, then back at the feedstore owner once more. Quiet at last, the fish lay glistening in the sun. On the Professor's round face the faintest crease of a smile began to form.

"It can't be," he murmured.

Donk snickered softly, shaking his head. "Ain't that somethin'? It's a goddamned carp."

From the crowd there exploded a sudden burst of awkward laughter, dying into silence, then laughter still more raucous as they pressed closer for a confirmation. Quickly satisfied, they drifted away in small noisy gaggles toward their cars. Soon only the Cronies remained with the fisherman, who still stood belly-deep in the water. In the net the fish again struggled to be free.

"Let him go," Donk commanded.

Pausing only to remove the fly embedded in a leathery lip, the Professor steadied the great fish in the pool and then lifted his hand. The carp finned in place for a moment, then sank like a lead weight and disappeared.

An hour later the conclave had gathered again back at the feedstore. Slouching against the counter, Shump Jumbeck made his case. "You caught him, but it wasn't no trout. That means you owe us a hundred dollars. The contract says it's a *trout* you had to catch." He looked for support from the glum faces around him. Finding none, he sat down on a fertilizer sack.

The Professor pulled out his checkbook. "It's true," he said. "That is what we agreed to. In any case, I caught him, but it wasn't done honorably. I owe you the amount at risk."

No one replied. The air filled with the scratch of the Professor's pen. Shump studied the broken laces on his workshoes. Harley Shepard took off his glasses and wiped at the lenses with his shirt. The others sat quietly, their eyes fixed on the floor.

"Just hold on a minute," Donk Muller bellowed, crumpling the proffered check and tossing it into an empty cream can. "If I recollect, the contract says you've got until sundown to catch the Reaper. And you ain't caught him yet. All you've caught is a big ole' yellow-backed carp."

For a long moment no one spoke. Then Harley Shepard cried, "You *ain't* caught the Reaper! He's still down there, down in those Narrows where nobody's ever even seen him good."

"That's right!" echoed Shump Jumbeck. "If you'd ever hooked the Reaper you'd know that couldn't of been him. The Reaper fights deep but he don't quit—not like some lard can you can haul up after three or four minutes."

The other Cronies gabbled in agreement as Donk stuffed the checkbook back in the Professor's shirt.

Darkness found them all reassembled in the lounge of a chophouse ten miles up the highway, a hundred-dollar bill on the table beside their drinks. At one end sat the Professor in a Shetland sweater with brown suede elbow patches; at the other Donk Muller in new overalls and a Massey-Ferguson cap. "A goldanged carp," he chuckled softly to himself.

"That thought he was the Reaper," added Harley Shepard, shaking his head.

At that the Professor raised his glass. "To that *hawg* of a trout that's somewhere down deep in The Narrows," he said firmly, nodding to each of the Cronies as they raised their drinks in replication. "I'll be back next spring to try him again."

"If I ain't caught him first," said Shump Jumbeck.

And he lowered his bottle to take a long swig from his beer.

Nests of Vipers

OPHIDIOPHOBIA. THE WORD GLIDES SINUOUSLY OFF
the tongue, coiling back on its own beginning. The syllables
spiral, the *o*'s rivet, the *i*'s flick. Mesmerized, faintly menaced,
you say it once more: *Ophidiophobia.*

"Fear of snakes" is what it means in the vernacular. Trust
me. I've been a textbook case for years.

It's an infirmity as hard to shake as it is easy to identify.
If you've got it, you know it. A formal diagnosis is as redundant
as a breath test on a flophouse drunk. The only point worth
debating is the severity of the affliction, an unknown until you
come face to face with your first snake. Nostrils flared and jaws
fused? The pulse rate of a cliff-crazed lemming? Your case is
light, close to nonexistent. If it's been a week and your sphincter

is still pinching off your prostate, you've got a slightly heavier dose.

Anyone can get hit, but the virulence runs highest in outdoorsmen. Again, trust me. It's from years of experience that I speak. *Anxiety* is a garter snake by the garage, the odd length of eel in your paella. *Ophidiophobia* is a bass pond after a guy tells you he saw a cottonmouth along the shoreline and is "pretty damned sure" he killed it with a rock.

Don't ask about causes. They're as shadowy as the depths of a Freudian psyche. Whom it strikes is a lottery. A random roll of the cosmic dice. Snake eyes. The kid next door drapes his pet boa around his neck like a pulsating winter muffler. You can't pick cucumbers from your garden without breaking into a cold sweat.

If the causes are cryptic, what determines the *degree* of one's affliction isn't. How hard you're hit is a matter of nurture, not nature; your case is settled during the impressionable years from two to twelve. My own childhood offers a clinical case in point:

Like most kids, I loved bedtime stories, and my mother was a great storyteller. Unfortunately, where snakes were concerned, her talent outstripped her range. I never heard about pet boas. Or snakes' shyness. Or how few species are actually venomous. What I did hear was a hundred archetypal variants of the Genesis myth.

They ran the gamut of dread, from Kipling's Rikki-Tikki-Tavi stalked by cobras to the lethal speed of a black mamba to the God-knows-whats that slithered through the sewers beneath the steam-shrouded streets of New York.

Then there was the tale she told me about her grandfather's neighbor raking hay in western Nebraska. The rake got clogged, the farmer reached down to clean the tines, and a prairie rattler hit him just below the left shoulder. Boot Hill.

I could go on. For Mom, a snake ranked with missing socks and the repeal of Prohibition as proof of the Powers of Darkness. Having already been sniffed out by every kid in school who had a length of coiled rubber and access to my lunchbox, I didn't see much reason to disagree.

Childhood passed into adolescence, adolescence into early manhood, with nothing more than such vicarious threats to my equanimity. It didn't help. Like all ophidiophobes, especially those unlucky enough to carry the simultaneous burden of growing up addicted to hunting and fishing, I knew they were simply the years of the ticking clock. The Big One was out there. The only question was where and when.

My moment came on a trip to a Wyoming ranch with three fly fishing compadres. We had driven all night, reached the ranch at dawn, and pulled onto the last dusty trail as the sun cleared the horizon. The end of the line was a canyon rim where a rusted-out cattle guard lay half buried under a sagging barbed-wire fence.

A shady place to park lay a few feet beyond, and I climbed out of Herb's car to free the gate from its thick tumbleweed tangle. I was about to hoist the gate hitch when something rustled near my left leg. Frozen, I glanced down. Two feet from my bootsoles, a snake disappeared into one of the cattle guard's open metal pipes.

The bodily wound was minor—barely noticeable, in fact, after I detached the small of my back from Herb's hood ornament. The mental wound went deeper. After a minute or so of breathing exercises, I picked up a splintered fencepost and crept warily toward the cattle guard. Unsure of the snake's identity,

I timidly rattled its cage. The pipe's instantaneous echo, as dry and sinister as death, was a fang mark across my psyche, a permanent scar.

Through the open windows behind me, where Herb, Butch, and Jimbo sat peering through the windshield, I heard the sound of nervous laughter. Five minutes later they stepped gingerly out of the car.

Leaving the vehicle where it sat, we strapped on our back-packs and skirted the weedy fence to a point a furlong or two beyond the cattle guard. Butch went over first, using his rod case the way a bomb-squad rookie might approach a trip wire with a set of tongs. The rest of us followed. Seventy-five yards from the fence, another rattlesnake slithered through the dust a few inches in front of Butch's sneakers. If there was laughter this time, I didn't hear it, because my shoulder blades had tightened over my ears.

When the moment had passed, the four of us hunkered down like a tight winter covey of quail, butt to butt, and formulated a strategy. We cut a branch from a trailside fir, put four rocks in Butch's hat, and agreed we'd alternate headmanning the others down five hundred yards of trail.

Jimbo lost the rock draw.

He tried to convince us we'd agreed on best two out of three.

He offered me his shoes and a Hardy reel for the old cowboy boots I was wearing. Then he said he'd throw in a grizzly neck.

Finally he started down the trail, waving the branch in front of him like a blind man witching for water. We had our point man. Since I'd drawn the lucky red rock, I brought up the rear, with Herb five feet ahead of me. He told me to protect our flanks.

In twenty minutes we had gone about the length of a football field when a startled jackrabbit exploded from the dry sagebrush a half-step ahead of Jimbo.

He stopped.

I could see his shoulders hunched under his backpack, the brim of his porkpie hat less than an inch from the collar of his shirt. He didn't turn around.

"Well, boys," he said, in a voice as soft as good bourbon. "I'd guess that's just about five hundred yards."

Butch, next in line, turned to Herb, his eyes never leaving the sagebrush. "Say, uh, Doc," he mumbled, "I've been meaning to ask you a question. Just what exactly do you plan to do if one of us does get nailed?" (We had all privately taken some measure of consolation from the fact that Herb was a physician. That he was a urologist was a fact each of us dealt with as best he could.)

Herb proceeded to give us a five-minute summary of what he remembered from medical school on field treatment of snakebite. As near as the rest of us could tell, there were about ten different theories, from acupuncture to packing the stricken member with ice. Good theories all, we discovered, each roughly as effective as all the others. Herb said he thought the overall success ratio was somewhere around fifty percent.

Jimbo wanted to know where we were going to get ice in July in the middle of a ranch in Wyoming.

Butch wanted to know if they put it on *every* member. Then he asked how high a rattlesnake could jump.

At that point Herb turned around slowly on the trail and looked back up the hill toward the car. "Y'know, boys," he said, "I hear the walleye have been hitting like hell up on Mille Lacs."

* * *

If you're a white-knuckle ophidi-
ophobe, such experiences are legion. They stick in your fragile
psyche like poisoned darts. Birth dates and anniversaries may
vanish from the memory with amnesiac regularity, but *nothing*
you've ever seen or heard is forgotten if it has to do with a
snake.

Years ago I saw a film shot in Arizona, probably a documen-
tary, no doubt rich with images of the plant and animal life of the
desert. I remember only one. A diamondback lies coiled and
motionless beneath a cactus as a kangaroo rat wanders feck-
lessly into the kill zone. He drills it the way you plink a rolling
beer can with a .22.

It's a curse I wouldn't wish on a cockroach. Still, for all its
agonies, ophidiophobia has a single redeeming quality that's
potentially of benefit to the outdoorsman: *No one recognizes
snake fever like another ophidiophobe.* If you're a hunter or
fisherman who likes his privacy, this knowledge is the psycho-
logical equivalent of steering a battered Ford through a crowded
parking lot where everybody else is stuck in a Lamborghini. It's
a potential edge.

Capitalizing on it requires minimal preparation. The first
step is to locate two or three sets of rattlesnake rattles and put
them in a small metal Band-Aid box. If you have a thespian flair,
I also recommend a snakeskin hatband and a pair of old hospital
bandages wrapped around the forearms. A Texas drawl adds to
the desired effect, as does the demonic gleam of a Charlie
Manson. Thus armed, simply wait for the next time an unwel-
come fisherman moves in on the pool you're fishing, giving you
the inevitable chance to strike.

Rarely does it take long, especially if you fish high-pressure
water in country where from time to time a snake has actually

been sighted. If the intruder is an ophidiophobe, you'll know it by the way he moves up the streamside trail:

1. Watch his eyes. Are they riveted to the ground, as if he's backtracking in search of a lost hip flask or fly box? 2. Check his rod. Is it carried low, down around the knees, the tip working over the grass ahead like a metal detector? 3. Study his reflexes. Does he twitch at the passing shadow of a bird, come out of his waders at the dry buzz of a flying grasshopper?

If the answer to all of the above is yes, it's show time.

I usually wait until the guy has approached to within thirty or forty yards, close enough to see the tight wrists and hear his shallow breathing. At this point I drop my rod suddenly on the bank, turn toward the weeds, and cup my ear. I maintain this attitude of tensed anticipation for a full thirty seconds, then pick up a small stick and creep forward slowly. By this time the intruder has arrived.

"Snake?" he says, in a thin coppery whisper.

(Note: If he doesn't say "Snake?"—if instead he says "Skunk?" or "What'd you hear?" or "The Hendrickson hatch come off yet?"—then you've misread the signs. The guy *was* looking for his fly box. If you've read the signs right, he'll say "Snake?" Guaranteed.)

More often than not they leave before you even get to the next step.

Occasionally, you'll run into an ophidiophobe with a bit more staying power, usually a guy stubborn or naive enough to believe it's an affliction he can kick. Don't let it discourage you. Just carry on with the shoreline clearance project, step two.

Start with a wild-eyed stomping through the weeds slashing your stick. If that doesn't suffice, try verbal amplification. Almost any idiom works, as long as the only place you could have learned it is Lubbock or Amarillo. "Call yo'selves snakes?" is one I like. So is "Why'ntcha buzzin' now? Yuh beady-eyed li'l bastards."

If even Panhandle rhetoric doesn't do it, you've still got the Band-Aid box.

Don't be in a hurry to use it. Wait for the sweat to bead along the intruder's jawline and the phobic question to form on his dehydrated lips. It's only a matter of time until he cracks.

When you're satisfied with his condition, stomp through the weeds one last time, viper-vexed, as if frustrated by the lack of action. Then toss the killing stick disgustedly across the creek. The rattles should click suggestively against the metal when you take the box from your vest, but lie still when you dump them in the trail dust. Finally, give him the answer he awaits:

"I ain't got 'em all, f'r damn sure, but I sure as hell got me two o' them sonsabitches!"

I've only known it to fail once, and even then it wasn't truly a failure. It happened to my friend Jimbo on the Sweetwater. He'd worked himself up to the final stomp-around stage when he stepped on a five-foot bullsnake. The poor devil hasn't wet a line since.

Fly Boy

THE CRONIES SAT GLUMLY IN DONK MULLER'S FEED-store. Though the room was flooded with late August sunshine, it wore a funereal air.

"I'm tellin' you he can't do it," Shump Jumbeck muttered, his stubbled face turned beseechingly toward the others for confirmation. "It ain't right."

No one responded. Harley Shepard lifted his coffee cup to his lips and slowly swallowed what remained of the viscous contents, his long-necked gulps audible across the dusty room. The only other sound was a fly's frustrated buzz as it bumped against a windowpane.

"It don't have to be *right*," the store's proprietor finally said, tossing his cigar butt toward an empty cream can. "It's legal. If he's got the money to buy it, he can do pretty much whatever he wants."

"*If* he's got the money?" Ralph McCrary snorted. "Shoot-fire, he's a banker, ain't he? He's got so damned much money he could prob'ly buy the whole goddamned crick!"

The words sliced through the heavy air with the finality of a meat cleaver. Again a full minute or more passed before anyone spoke.

"We got to *try* somethin'," Shump said. "I been fishin' that water since I was barely big enough to tell a decent-sized trout from a tree stump. We're talkin' about the Railroad Hole!"

"We all know what we're talkin'," Harley Shepard interrupted. "It's like wakin' up in a hospital and findin' out they've hacked off one o' your legs. But what else can we try? The bastard's got the money, and he won't listen to common sense."

"Bunker," Ralph McCrary spat. "Bunker the goddamned banker. He's like that fella down in Texas that tried to buy up all them silver bricks."

"We got to try somethin'," Shump said.

But there was in truth nothing they hadn't tried, and every man in the room knew it. Since the day six weeks earlier when the bank president had first walked into Vera's Cafe and asked who owned the half-mile stretch of meadow along the abandoned railway—rumors of his late-night purchase moving through Frieburg the next morning like ripples on a windswept lake—the Cronies had tried all they could. And been stonewalled. They had spent hours pressuring the seventy-year-old farmer who owned the land to reconsider, silenced at last by the size of the banker's offer and the old man's yearnings to live out his years in town. They had driven the sixty miles to Colchester and grudgingly bought a half-hour with the town's most celebrated lawyer, who had proffered not so much as the tiniest loophole in return. They had marched dispiritedly out of his office and on up the street to their tormentor's bank—and been stopped cold by a golden-haired secretary.

Finally, in desperation, they had followed the red Porsche to the Railroad Hole on four successive Friday evenings in a dogged ritual of rejection, each progressively more curt and condescending, until in the end hope gave way to simple harassment of a stiffnecked fool.

They had tried it all.

"We got to try somethin'," Shump said.

"Try *what?*" Ralph McCrary shot back, slapping a sack of feed in exasperation. "Slash his tires and put sand in his gas tank?"

"Beat him to death with that fancy gold case he uses for his rod?"

The Frieburg handyman bit his lip sullenly in answer. The horsefly behind him continued to bludgeon itself on the windowpane.

"We could . . ." He stopped in mid-sentence, his voice cracking at the magnitude of the proposal he was about to offer. "We could pool our money and try to buy it back."

The others looked at him as if he'd just suggested they let their hair grow and make a demo tape as a country rock band.

"I'm serious," he added defensively. "Donk's doin' good. Ralph's been saltin' away all those Social Security checks. The price o' hogs where it's at, Harley's sure as hell got to be makin' himself some money. I've even got a few bucks—"

"How much is 'a few'?" Ralph McCrary cut in. No one else in the store moved, all eyes turned skeptically toward the rumpled entrepreneur in jeans and grease-spotted T-shirt. No one before had ever known him to volunteer possession of so much as a twenty-dollar bill.

"I don't know. . . ." He shuffled his feet uncomfortably. "Coupla' hundred mayb—"

Sardonic hoots filled the room, smothering whatever financial revelations were to follow. Shaking his head, Harley Shepard rose to refill his coffee cup.

"Two hundred dollars," he said. "Two hundred dollars might buy you twenty foot o' riffle water down in the Cedar Swamp."

"But he wants us to *pool,* Shep," Ralph McCrary corrected. "Don't forget that. Pool ever'thing so's we can buy us a whole potload o' pools."

Donk looked up from his account book and waited quietly until the mocking laughter had subsided. Only the ponderous silence of resignation now filled the room.

"There prob'ly ain't a snowball's chance in hell he'd be int'rested," the proprietor mumbled, biting the tip off a fresh King Edward, "but we might as well drive out there one more time to try. It's gettin' on toward five o'clock, and it's Friday. An hour from now he'll be standin' crotch deep in the Railroad Hole. I'll throw in half o' what he give for the place myself if we can come up with a decent offer."

The Railroad Hole was worth it. Five miles west of town, Crooked Creek flanked the weedy tracks of a defunct connecting line through a meadow stretch of deep-water runs and riffles, bending away after a half-mile into the Cedar Swamp. At its upper end, a hundred yards below the house occupied since birth by the septuagenarian who had recently been persuaded to sell it, the dark water cut sharply around the concrete and timber pilings of a rusted railroad bridge. Eight or nine feet deep at its head, its gravel bottom studded with decades of rail-repair detritus, the Railroad Hole was water to make even a beginning angler's eyes take on an avaricious gleam.

It had happened six weeks before to Judson Price. Brought to the pool by one of his tellers a few days after his return from a vacation on Martha's Vineyard—where he'd been persuaded by an old Princeton classmate to join him for three days at a fly-casting school in Vermont—the banker had leapt into his newfound sport with the fervor of a religious zealot. His eyes had been freed of scales. A driven perfectionist whose few previous hours of recreation had largely been occupied on fairway and squash court, he had sufficient grace to fall passionately in love with fly fishing from the first moment a line unfurled properly over his head. A day later he had bought a Garrison rod. A week later he'd arranged a Christmas trip to New Zealand. He had become a trout fisherman.

But to the locals who waited for him now under the shade of a dying elm tree in Horst Patzner's barnyard, he didn't know a damned thing about fishing for trout.

"Look at him," Shump muttered, cranking up his window against the trailing dust as the red Porsche swept by and stopped beside a sagging grain bin. "What the hell kind of man goes fishing in a car like that?"

"Bunker!" Ralph McCrary hissed with a rancor usually reserved for politicians and dumb football coaches. His voice held an unmistakable trace of awe, nonetheless.

The banker did in fact cut a regal figure. Sliding his six-foot-plus frame from the car's leather interior, he stood for a moment to stretch languidly like a jungle cat in the sunlight, as if oblivious of the locals who sat watching not thirty yards away. The Rolex gleamed. The silk tie and suit were a page from *Gentlemen's*

Quarterly. Matching streaks of gray feathered back along the sides of his thick brown hair like the quills of a Leadwing Coachman.

Offering his overfamiliar suppliants not so much as a disdainful glance, he opened the trunk and reached in for a canvas travel bag. Setting it on the roof, he pulled the Garrison from its monogrammed case, clamped on a reel, and began threading line through the guides.

"What kind of S.O.B. would get his rod rigged up before he even takes off his work clothes?" McCrary added.

"Always the same," Donk answered. "Next he'll unzip the bag and pull out that fancy fishing vest that looks like it just got dry-cleaned."

The angler did exactly that, as the feedstore owner continued:

"Now he'll reach into the lower right-hand pocket and take out a pair of glasses with lenses about half an inch thick."

"What the hell?" Shump said. "He got bad eyes or just tryin' to look intelligent?"

"Who knows? But ever' time you watch him he does it the same way. You can bet your last dollar on it."

"If he had a dollar," Harley Shepard interrupted.

"One he ain't been savin' up to put in the pool," Ralph McCrary said.

The old man behind the steering wheel ignored the raillery and went on, as if to himself, his eyes riveted on the painstaking rites continuing:

"Now he'll put on the glasses and take a fly box from the lower left-hand pocket. He'll look over what's inside like it's the crown jewels, then pull out a fly and commence to tie it on like he's doin' heart surgery on the President. After that he'll put the glasses back in the vest, fold it up, and lay it on the car roof, then make a few practice casts over that patch o' cabbage. Then he'll lay his rod on the vest and head for the barn to change his duds."

Five minutes later as the banker disappeared behind the barn door with his duffel, Shump delivered the epilogue: "If I had a gard'ner snake right now I'd walk over and drop it inside that vest."

What the four locals did instead was wait.

They waited until the angler strode back from the barn newly clad in twill shirt, Irish cap, and neoprene waders. Then they climbed out of the car and confronted him beside the Porsche.

"Damnit, men," he said, indifferently polishing the amber lenses of his sunglasses. "Isn't this getting a tad redundant? I've told you repeatedly the earnest money's been paid and I've already run the whole package by a builder. Face facts. It's a done deal."

"It ain't right," Shump Jumbeck objected. "There's been Patzners livin' on this land for a hundred years. You can't just bulldoze the whole place down like so much scrub timber and put up a bunch of them condoms . . . condomsini—"

"You're totally confused," the banker interrupted, lifting his vest off the car and slipping it over his muscular shoulders. "It's a corporate *park*. I'm retaining only the upper twenty acres. The rest will be sold discreetly in separate parcels to parties whose environmental credentials will be—I can assure you—absolutely blue chip. Most will be anglers like myself who are looking for nothing more than an accessible retreat for the weekend. Only the shoreline ambience will be altered. Crooked Creek isn't going to change."

"Like hell it won't," Ralph McCrary shouted. "You can't seem to get it through your thick nut, but what we're talkin' about here is genuine big-trout water, has been for God knows how many years. You can't put up half a dozen houses with lawns shaved down to the shoreline and kids splashin' around on float tubes or jumpin' in off a bunch o' goddamned swingin' bridges. Not if you want anything left but some stubby-finned stocked little pissants. Your big trout's not gonna live in a place like that!"

"I release the trout I catch. And I fish—as you should— primarily for the aesthetic. Crooked Waters will allow dozens of fine people of all ages a brush with Nature. Weighed against that reality, your promise of taking the occasional large fish hardly resonates."

"You ever caught one?" Shump Jumbeck challenged, his voice quivering with indignation.

The banker's face reddened, and he held his Ray-Bans toward the sun, squinting. Then he turned abruptly and lifted his rod off the Porsche.

"That's beside the point," he said. "I can assure you I'm far happier bringing a handful of lively ten-inchers to net than I would be lugging in one of your mythic monsters." With that he leaned down, flicked the door lock, and set off toward the Railroad Hole.

The feedstore owner's battered Ford had reached the township limit of Frieburg before the ensuing silence was broken. "We got to *do* somethin'," Shump Jumbeck said, "And we got to do it fast."

This time not even Ralph McCrary could summon sufficient will to tell him the fight was over. The car idled to a stop behind the feedstore. No one opened a door to get out.

"We got to call the Professor," Shump said.

Three days later, a steamy Monday with the noon temperature already hovering in the high nineties, the old Ford moved slowly back up the same highway. This time it held only the driver and another squat figure dressed in khaki safari shirt and trail shorts.

"We thought mebbe you could make him see," Donk said. "You've got a way with words. Mebbe you can make him listen."

"I'm not sanguine about the prospect," the Professor answered, dabbing with a folded handkerchief at the perspiration beading on his flushed forehead. "Mr. Jumbeck has given me to believe you've left precious few stones unturned."

"No question about that, but the young fella never did hear our offer. With what you're willin' to throw in, it's almost four thousand more'n what he give for the place not quite a month and a half ago. You ever met a man so dumb he wouldn't at least consider a deal that sweet?"

The car rolled on past fields of corn and alfalfa. Bins and silos. The acrid fragrance of a dusty feedlot. Heat shimmered off the blacktop and radiated through the windshield.

"Tell me all you know about this chap," the Professor finally responded. "His actions, appearance, idiosyncracies. If one must enter the lists scant of weaponry, he ought at least to have the strategic advantage of his man."

For fifteen minutes the driver talked and his passenger listened, occasionally grunting or stroking his beard but offering not the slightest interruption. He was silent even after the narrator had ended his monologue and rolled to a stop at a crossing for a passing train.

The freight rumbled by as the two men stared idly out the open windows. To the right a small roadside lake lay flat and still, its overheated water choked with moss. A single panfisherman drowsed on the sandy shore in a lawn chair next to a beer cooler. A pair of near-naked children played in the shallows fifty yards away. Whooping, the smaller of them plucked a shoreline reed and carried it in her mouth as she splashed out a few feet to where the pea-green water was slightly deeper. Then she dove and stayed under for thirty or forty seconds, breathing through the hollow stalk.

"There's your Railroad Hole in a couple o' years," Donk said, easing the car once again into motion. The Professor turned briefly toward him as if distracted, then took a last look back at the lake. Several more minutes passed before he spoke.

"If memory serves, you have a ten-year-old grandson?"

"That's right," Donk said, raising his eyebrows at the non sequitur. "Ten or eleven, one."

"Is the lad at all adept as a swimmer?"

"Willy?" the driver chuckled, ashes from his cigar butt dusting the ample front of his overalls. "You wouldn't have to ask if you'd ever been out with him when the fish aren't cooperatin'. You can't keep the little nipper in his britches. He's a real water rat."

The Professor nodded and stroked his white beard as if pondering a thorny passage in Herodotus. Then he mumbled something inaudible and pulled out his briar pipe.

"Turn the car around, Donk," he said. "Let's head home. His own turf is no place to engage an adversary. I think we can find a more propitious venue for our little *guerre de position* with Mr. Price."

And for the next thirty minutes the driver listened in an advancing state of stupefaction as the car retraced its route over the shimmering asphalt. The Professor stopped talking, in fact, only when he climbed out of the Ford in front of the feedstore and marched resolutely up the street to where his own car was parked.

"Remember," he said, glancing briefly over his shoulder. "One o'clock sharp Friday. Have young William at the railroad bridge for a dress rehearsal. In the meantime, I have some research to complete."

Shump Jumbeck emerged from the cafe and trotted anxiously across the street as the ancient Austin-Healey disappeared around a corner.

"You're back already?" he said accusingly. "What happened—the Professor chicken out?"

The proprietor paused at the feedstore's weathered door, skeleton key in hand, then distractedly pushed it open.

"He's either gonna make us all look like bigger fools than Buck Storkamp when he went broke tryin' to raise that field o' those puffball mushrooms," he said. "Or we got a chance."

At five o'clock Friday afternoon the Cronies clustered behind a wooden gate a short distance below the Railroad Hole, their car hidden in a nearby cornfield. They gaped in varying degrees of comprehension at the strange scene unfolding a few feet away.

The boy familiar to them for years as "Little Willy" now stood transformed as if kidnapped by invaders from Atlantis, his small body sheathed in a wetsuit. His hands were tightly gloved and his towhead covered by a rubber swimming cap. Atop it perched a dive mask, the tempered-glass faceplate and nose pocket poised for lowering over his freckled face. Strapped to his back like a small black bomb was an air canister the size of a workman's thermos, its valve connected to a mouthpiece by two feet of rubber hose.

As the Cronies gawked, the Professor pulled from a bag and buckled around the boy's waist one last bewildering appendage—a weighted belt from which floated half a dozen small green balloons knotted to six-inch strings. From a distance, it appeared he wore a girdle of melons on his narrow hips.

"Mind now," the scholar lectured, hands resting on his pupil's thin shoulders. "Three stages. Use the watch. Precisely ten minute intervals between."

"Yessir," the boy said. The eyes in his upturned face were those of a goatherd before Jehovah.

"When you're not in the water, perch out of sight under the bridge. Stay completely submerged until you've made the turn around the abutment. You have more than twenty minutes of air in the pony bottle, so relax and concentrate."

"Yessir."

"Remember, save the belt for Stage Two. Be careful when you hang it on the piling nail lest the balloons burst."

And with a soft dub on the backside, the Professor sent his young knight off in the direction of the rusty bridge.

Twenty minutes later the red Porsche swung down the farm lane and braked to a stop, large dust cloud billowing. The driver climbed out, stretched, then took off his coat and tie. The conspirators watched nervously from behind the slatted gate.

"Don't change nothin'," Donk intoned, his fingers working nervously up and down his suspenders. "For the love o' mercy don't go changin' nothin' now."

"It all depends on the fly and the vest," the Professor whispered. "If he doesn't tie on the fly and leave the vest briefly unattended we're finished before we begin."

As if wired to a control switch, the banker pulled out the canvas bag, rigged the Garrison, and began false casting over the garden. It was the loving stroke of a man hearing the liquid rhythms of a favorite symphony swelling in his head. Not until the last chord had died, several minutes later, did he lay the rod on the car roof and head for the barn.

"Now!" said the Professor, squeezing the elbow of the

figure in tennis shoes crouching anxiously next to him. "Do it deftly. And take care to leave the vest exactly as it's found!"

With surprising speed for a man on the far side of forty, Shump Jumbeck sprinted up the cattle path.

"Last time I seen Shump run like that, he was bustin' his hump headin' for McCool Junction's goal line," Ralph McCrary croaked. "Playoff game his senior season."

"The time he fumbled on the four?" Harley Shepard said.

The watchers rose in tense expectancy as the runner reached his destination, his body crouched, his eyes fixed on the barn.

"Easy," Ralph McCrary hissed. "Do it easy. Don't screw it up now."

Apparently satisfied he hadn't been heard, the runner seized the vest and extracted a small rectangular case from one of the lower pockets. Then he refolded it, checked once more to be sure he hadn't been discovered, and hastily jammed whatever he had stolen into his jeans. He scuttled back down the hill to a muffled but euphoric pummeling by his peers.

A minute later the angler emerged in cap and waders to don his vest. Humming a Broadway show tune, he advanced on the Railroad Hole.

For a recent initiate, observed the Professor, the Colchester banker was a remarkably proficient caster. The small fly alit on the placid water at the pool's lower end with the lightness of a windblown feather. Three casts later, he had caught and carefully released an eight-inch brown.

Dressing the fly, he again fed out coils of line and entered the stream to stand now where the current flowed gently around his ankles, fishing the slightly faster water above. Within fifteen minutes he had caught two fish more.

"Not yet," the Professor whispered intently. "Stay on the piling until you can see the fly."

"Willy can handle it," Donk said. "He'll do it the way you practiced."

Stripping out more line, the angler eased warily forward, casting to the deep broken water that swirled and eddied in a sharp elbow around the bridge abutment. A tentative step or two later, he stood crotch-deep in the lower pool.

"Now," the Professor murmured. "Into the water. Stage One!"

Fifty feet of line unfurled, and the small Adams dropped a few inches to the left of a rotted timber. The fly rode lightly downstream, untouched. The angler lifted it off the water, false cast, and dropped it once more on the same jaunty pathway.

It floated perhaps fifteen inches. Then the water exploded in a thunderclap of spray as the angler's line went taut and the rod was nearly wrenched from his fingers. Scrambling frantically for position, he held on as the throbbing line gave two more jerks so violent the rod tip plunged momentarily underwater, then went dead. The fury had lasted no more than three seconds. Flaccid coils of line and leader now drifted toward him in mute anticlimax.

The angler stood motionless as the line bunched around his hips and trailed limply downstream behind him, the tip of his rod dipping in the current like the bill of a shorebird run amok. So uncontrollably were his hands shaking it appeared the rod might fall from his grasp.

"Gawddog!" Ralph McCrary murmured, gaping with the others from their command post. "What the hell . . . ?"

"Must of been a big'un," Donk chortled, winking at the bearded officer on his right.

The angler stumbled out of the creek and sank heavily to

his knees in the meadow. He stared at the upper pool like an infantryman scanning the ground ahead after the sudden detonation of a mine.

A hundred yards below, the Professor stared at the pool with the same hypnotic intensity. "Patience," he whispered, glancing at his wristwatch. *"Semper in tempore* good lad."

Five minutes later, the dazed angler lifted his rod off the grass and slowly began to retrieve the line still snaking along shore in the riffle. His eyes even then did not leave the pool.

"Now!" urged the Professor, glancing again at his watch. "Stage Two, young William. The balloons!"

The words had scarcely died on the commander's lips when the angler leaped to his feet as if stung in the flank by a hornet. Ten feet below the bridge, the pool's surface had suddenly swollen with a boil the size of a manhole cover. Twenty seconds later it happened again.

Seizing his broken tippet, the angler unzipped half a dozen vest pockets in a fumbling search for his fly box. Finally locating it, he sank again to his knees and violently tugged open the zipper above his right hip.

With an audible gasp, he froze.

Dropping the rod, he patted the empty pocket with quivering fingers, which then scurried up and down his chest in a wild burlesque of a man plagued by a loose mouse inside his sweater, finally tearing off the vest and scattering the contents on the grass where he rummaged through them as if deranged.

"Desperate man," said Donk.

"What ought to take better care o' his belongings," said Shump Jumbeck.

The pool's surface broke again with an audible bulge as the angler raised his head in a keening cry of anguish, then seized the fly box and snatched another Adams from the dozen he'd brought home from New England. Squeezing half an inch of tippet between his right thumb and forefinger, he stabbed it again and again at the tiny eyelet, pausing only to wipe the sweat furiously from his eyes.

"Looks like he could use a sewin' lesson," Ralph McCrary offered.

As he spoke the surface of the pool bulged with an angry swelling the size of a small Jacuzzi. "Godawmighty!" he added, "What the hell did you two give that kid?"

"Musta hit a double," Donk mumbled, winking again at the orchestrator.

"The lad's inventive," said the Professor, chuckling with respect.

The banker now lay flat on his back, left eye closed, the tiny fly held at arm's length directly above him. A litany of curses rose skyward as he feverishly jabbed the stub of tippet upward toward the late-afternoon light.

"Think the moment's come, Donk?" the Professor queried, arching his woolly eyebrows.

"Don't guess there's much reason to wait. Be downright unneighborly not to offer a helpin' hand to a blind man."

With that the feedstore owner picked up a casting rod and a battered tackle box and ambled slowly down to the creek bank. Coughing to make his presence known, he waddled up the streamside trail.

The banker jumped up at the sound and bounded, rod in hand, across the riffle to meet him, sweat streaking his forehead. His tight face creased in a sudden smile of ingratiation as he spoke.

"Old Sport, how ya doin' tonight?"

"Doin' good," answered the proprietor. "Yourself?"

"Not bad. Not bad at all." The banker paused for a moment, then bent to pluck a spear of foxtail. "I was wondering," he drawled, "if you'd mind doing me a little favor."

"Whats'at?" The old man grinned.

Encouraged, the angler plunged onward. "I can't understand it, but I seem somehow to have misplaced my reading glasses. Would you be sporting enough to tie on this—" He was holding out the fly as the water behind him erupted like a small hot spring.

"Damn!" said his fellow rod-carrier, staggering a few steps forward. "You see the size o' that formrise? That's got to be the biggest hawg in this hole since Luke Luedtke landed Old Willieboy back in sixty-eight!" Fumbling in his tackle box, he proceeded to pull out a silver spinner the length of a small grappling hook.

"No!" the banker shouted. "It's *my* fish! You can't do this. It belongs to me!"

The proprietor looked up abruptly, eyes narrowed, the rod gripped like a short lance in his gnarled fingers. He wasn't smiling now.

"I can't?" he said. "Ain't you forgettin' somethin', Mister? You mebbe put down some money for this place, but you don't take legal possession 'till the middle of September. And that fish ain't gonna be *yours* even then. Any man smart enough to own a bank ought to damned sure know a trout like that don't never *belong* to nobody. Not even if you're lucky enough in your lifetime to hook one and get him in."

The two men stood motionless beside the stream, their incandescent eyes fixed on one another. Ten seconds of theater played in silence against evening birdsong and the timeless warble of the creek.

"I'd give a helluva lot just to make one cast to that trout," the angler finally murmured, his gaze falling wistfully across the water.

The old man nodded. His knuckles loosened around the rod grip.

"He's one of the best," he said. "I can guarantee it. . . . Course he don't quite match that truckful o' stockers you'll have in here this time next year."

The other man flushed. Slowly his fingers too loosened around the Garrison. He looked away toward the ridgetop as he spoke.

"I was wrong," he said.

"I'll be damned," Ralph McCrary muttered, speaking for those downstream who watched the ensuing handshake in slack-jawed amazement. "I wouldn't of believed it could be done."

The conspirators gaped through the gate slats as their stumpy peer proceeded to knot on a fly for the angler who towered nearly a full head above him, his lean body tensed like a wolfhound straining at the leash. When the knot was done, the fisherman hastily dressed the fly and crept into the riffle on tiptoe, false casting as he advanced.

"Stage Three," whispered the Professor. "A trifle sadistic, but it's imperative to set the hook."

Five minutes later the angler stumbled drunkenly for the second time that evening from the Railroad Hole's dark, al-chemical waters, eyes glazed and trailing slack line. Five mourn-ers waited to offer heartfelt condolences at his loss.

An hour later the wake continued in Vera's Cafe behind beaded glasses of iced tea perched on a linoleum tabletop.

"Only once in my experience, on the Beaverhead, when a stiff west wind set a large hatch of caddis flies skittering," the Professor nodded solemnly, his face turned toward the slumped

figure in neoprene waders across from him, mouth slightly
agape. "It's rare indeed for a fish to take a dry fly with the
savagery you describe."

"They say that's how Old Willieboy hit," Shump Jumbeck
drawled, raising his glass toward Vera for a refill. "Course that
was a little before my time."

"We're still waitin' for your time," muttered Ralph
McCrary.

The angler shook his head incredulously and spread his
long arms a foot beyond the length of the pockmarked table. "He
was that big—I swear to God," he said, his voice quavering like
that of a man just returned from El Dorado. "I got a glimpse of
him a second before he turned the corner and snapped off my
leader on that bridge support."

"Could be," said Donk Muller. "That stretch o' water's
always held some hellacious fish."

Outside the cafe at nightfall, the Cronies bid farewell as the
banker trudged slowly up the sidewalk, numbly clutching the
cased glasses one of the locals had somehow found adrift in
Crooked Creek. As he approached his car, a small boy on a new
bicycle suddenly sped out of an alley and wobbled recklessly up
the street past him, a damp shock of blond hair matted across
his forehead.

"Wouldn't of guessed he could ride a bike that big," mumbled one of the Cronies.

The boy's grandfather flashed a gap-toothed grin at the
Professor. "Four foot high and risin'," he bragged. He seemed
about to add something more, then paused for a long moment,
as if intent on the disappearing taillights of the Porsche.

"Somethin' I been meanin' to ask you," he finally said,
taking a cigar from his pocket.

"Yes?"

"About this fly fishin'." The old man slipped the cigar from its wrapper and turned it over in his palm meditatively. "I was just wonderin'. Next week when you're teachin' that young dog a few more new tricks. . . . You feel inclined to take a crack at an old one?"

Testaments from the Blind

THERE'S SOMETHING ABOUT A DUCK BLIND THAT eventually turns even the levelest heads a little loco. Maybe it's all those "slow" days, when grown men stand for hours staring blankly at an empty sky. Or maybe it's the weather. Whatever the reasons, duck hunters are different.

There are a lot of people, of course, who swear that *all* hunters are crazy. These are usually the same folks who think fishermen tell time by six-pack and speak an aboriginal form of English limited to regional variants of "Hooooboy." Compared to the duck hunter, however, even the most fanatic upland bird shooter looks normal. The truth is, for sheer numbers of odd-balls and all-around world-class eccentrics, waterfowlers are in a league of their own.

My own introduction to this truth came in the form of one

Gund H. Bunderson, the not so humble possessor of the best blind in Wabasha County. A gaunt Scandinavian with a chin that could have chiseled pine, he was known to everyone on the river simply as Moses. On those raw November days when a polar wind raked the water to a steel-blue chop, the mallards bellied down on his backwater pocket like softball players converging on a keg of free beer.

From our own blinds—the closest no more than a tantalizing two hundred yards or so up the windswept shoreline—we would watch flock after flock sail behind us high over the poplars, then suddenly brake, spin, and tumble down on Moses like falling leaves. On such days the old Norwegian invariably picked up a further appellation. "Gawddamned Moses," one of us would thickly mumble through lips the color of plum jelly. "That gawddamned Moses doin' it again."

What made our plight all the more painful was the knowledge that a place in his blind could be had simply for the asking. Moses hadn't had a steady partner for years, not since the day Doc Douglas dropkicked his thermos into the river, sank his decoy boat, and waddled the three miles back to town in breast waders. As time passed and the ducks continued to treat our sets like so many colonies of lepers, most of us finally cracked under the pressure and took our own turn at Moses' side. Once. I know guys who sold their shotguns and took up broomball when the impulse to share the old man's blind began to build once again.

Perhaps because I could actually remember the last time I had seen a duck close enough to identify its gender, I held out longer than anybody else. I didn't succumb, in fact, until the afternoon I realized that the highball was the only call I still knew how to blow.

Moses was in his garage cleaning a limit of greenheads

when I drove out to see him later that evening. Four inches of new-fallen snow blanketed the ground, and a biting northwest wind whistled through the trees.

"See you had some luck," I ventured, repressing an impulse to bend down and touch the nearest mallard.

"Verily," Moses answered. He stopped plucking and looked at me sagely over the tops of his wire-rimmed glasses.

"Any chance, uh, that you might . . . you know . . . have a place for another hunter tomorrow morning?" I prepared myself for the worst. Moses never turned anybody down.

He dropped the drake on the floor and slowly picked up another one from a wicker basket. "Be ready in the hour before dawn," he commanded, "and let your loins be well girded about. Like unto an unfeathered bird is the man ill-prepared for weather."

The first thing Moses mentioned when he picked me up the next morning was that his dog was feeling poorly and wouldn't crawl out of his kennel. Unfortunately, I failed to heed the omen. At that point I was more concerned with the afflictions of his ancient pickup and his efforts to hold it on the snow-packed river road.

We managed to make it to a turnout beside a narrow trail that had been bushwhacked through the willows, and I was about to start down it when Moses announced he would carry my gun and shells. "Awful nice of you to offer," I said, shocked at his generosity. "But, hey, I won't have any trouble. I'm quite a bit younger than you." The guys weren't going to believe how much the crusty old coot had changed.

Turning on his flashlight, Moses focused it on a bulging gunny sack that sagged against the pickup's tailgate. It was filled with spare mallard floaters weighted with railroad spikes. "Be not stiffnecked," he grumbled, lifting the gun from my shoulder and setting off toward the willows. "His duty falls even unto the man of hoary head."

Dawn was already breaking by the time we reached the blind, and I dropped the heavy sack and headed straight for Moses' decoy boat, assuming he was following behind. He wasn't. Instead, he stood on shore in the dim light with a wading staff in his hand, pointing to the pocket where he wanted me to spread the stool.

"Rejoice, O young man, in thy youth," he called, as I struggled to drag the boat across a gravel bar into the river. "Hasten to thy labors. Unseemly as the hinderparts of a goat are the actions of the slothful man."

I had set the last decoy and was towing the empty boat back toward the willows, when again I heard him commanding:

"Kneel! Kneel in the water!"

The order was so urgent I instinctively dropped to my knees as if poleaxed, staying crouched even as a stream of icewater lipped my waders and trickled down my right leg. At about the same moment I caught the flash of flaring wings and heard Moses' double-barrel belch a single volley. A drake splashed down on the outer edge of the backwater, fifty yards beyond the decoys. In the current's heavy chop it began at once to drift away downstream.

"Hasten thy feet!" Moses shouted, waving his arms wildly. "Rejoice for nature's bounty in the suppleness of thy limbs!"

By the time I'd slogged through the backwater, trotted down a weed-choked sandbar, and wallowed across the channel to head off the mallard, I had finished rejoicing. The sun had risen above the willows when I finally made it back to the blind.

"Happy is the man of vigor," Moses responded, snatching the duck from my fingers and dropping it beside his gear.

"I've got a bootful of water," I said. "My feet are cold, and I have yet to put a shell in my shotgun."

Moses refilled his pipe, then slowly bent over to pick up his ditty bag. "Woes without number are visited on the imprudent man," he mumbled, dropping the bag and handing me a dry pair of socks.

I had grudgingly accepted them and was standing barefoot in my underwear just outside the blind, draining my waders, when once again I heard the old man hissing urgently under his breath:

"Birds in the air! Cloak thy gaudy buttocks!"

I had no choice but to crouch once more as a flock of about thirty widgeons swung upriver just outside the decoys. Shaking in the cold, I hunkered down as they made several slow, wary circles, finally cupped their wings, and came in. Moses rose and fired both barrels. Two drakes hit the river like stones. Pants draped around my ankles, I reached my gun just in time to give a parting salute to a straggler climbing toward the ionosphere. Five quiet seconds later, the pellets rained down on top of us, rattling the shoreline reeds.

"Much seed does the tardy man sow," Moses proclaimed, wading out with his staff to retrieve the ducks that floated belly-up on the water. "But little does he reap."

When he returned I reloaded my gun and took stock of the situation. Three fat ducks lay neatly stacked in a corner at the other end of the blind; I hadn't shot a one. Moses was dry; my legs were wet from crotch to chilblains. Moses had yet to break a sweat; I felt as if I'd just pulled a plow across forty acres of lowland gumbo. No question, it was time to take a stand.

"You've got a thermos of hot coffee in that bag," I growled, "and a package of sugar doughnuts. I want some."

Moses regarded me with a look I hadn't seen since I told my wife our sewer had backed up in the basement.

"Heed not the belly," he intoned. "Sooner put a log in thy throat than be a man given to appetite."

I took a step closer.

"A gold ring in a swine's snout is the youth of intemperate nature," he said, reaching for the bag.

"I'm forty-five years old," I rejoined. "Hand me the thermos."

It's amazing how much better a man can feel after four cups of coffee and six or seven doughnuts. To be perfectly honest, my spirits had revived so much I silently swore the next duck would hit the water before Moses had hoisted his gun. If I were really quick I might be able to drop a pair before his creaking fingers had fired a single barrel.

My chance for revenge wasn't long in coming. Five minutes later a single mallard drake came winging low up the river, saw the decoys, and bored in. He was obviously not even going to take a swing. Moses was just reaching for his gun, in fact, when I sprang up and fired a hurried round head-on at the greenhead, then another, then a third. With the shots still reverberating in my ears, Moses rose, tracked the drake like a carpenter sizing up the day's last piece of wallboard, and folded it cleanly as it flared high above the blind. The duck came crashing down in the willows ten feet from where we stood.

Neither of us said a thing while I quietly reloaded and Moses shuffled out to make the retrieve. Back in the blind, after pouring himself the half-cup of coffee I'd left in his dinged silver thermos, he peered over the tops of his glasses and took a long, slurping sip.

"The young man and the hungry dog," he mumbled. "Ever overhasty."

I asked him if he'd managed to find the thermos he lost the last day he hunted with Doc.

It wasn't too much later that a north wind began to blow so hard I had trouble keeping my eyes from glazing over, and in a matter of minutes the temperature plummeted. The spray that coated the decoys quickly froze to a thin glare ice. Clearly, I didn't have a lot more time to get my point across.

"We've got four ducks," I said, giving the old man the steeliest glare I could muster. "You've shot every one."

"If a bear happen upon a honeypot, bountifully is he blessed."

"I'm not sure you caught my drift," I said. "Maybe it's the wind. We've got fifteen minutes left to hunt, tops, and you've taken an entire limit. I have yet to scratch a feather."

"Fortunate the man in need when his neighbor step forth as a helpmate," Moses answered. "Unhappy the laborer with a broken plough."

"Can't you hear?" I shouted. "I haven't shot one lousy duck the entire time we've been out here!"

"If thy shooting eye offend thee, pluck it out."

It suddenly occurred to me he might respond better to a more philosophical approach.

"See that big glob of mud that's stuck on the bow of your decoy boat?" I said, nodding toward the willows. "Think a guy could clean it off with a load of magnum fours?"

For what it's worth, I shot the last duck, which turned out to be a merganser. It dropped on the outer edge of the backwater, fifty yards beyond the decoys.

The Turkeywood Papers

A FEW YEARS AGO, IN A MOMENT OF WEAKNESS, I applied for a "wild turkey permit." My name was drawn. After spending several weeks reading countless how-to articles and blowing lascivious practice notes through a latex diaphragm, I set off in pursuit of a creature reputed to be the cagiest in the woods.

I did it all again the following April. And then I kept on doing it, whenever my number turned up in the draw.

Aside from baggy eyes, permanently altered sleeping habits, and the weary slouch of a pack-hauling Sherpa, I found the experience left me with one overpowering impression: If the ultimate proof of a creature's caution is invisibility, I was after a bird that ranked with Sasquatch and the Loch Ness Monster on anybody's wariness scale.

I have yet to shoot a wild turkey. I have yet to see a wild turkey. I don't even *know* anybody who has ever seen a wild turkey. And I say all this after spending God knows how many mornings out and about in the woods.

It's true, once or twice I heard some throaty clucks that resembled those vibrating from the disk wedged sideways in my larynx. And a few other times there echoed from a distant ridgetop the kind of tremulous warble I hadn't heard since Robbie Briggs stuck heat-balm in our eighth-grade gym teacher's shorts. But the bird itself? Not a trace. I might as well have been searching for Jimmy Hoffa.

I mention all this as prologue to the revelation that follows. For last April, huddled under an oak tree waiting out the end of a heavy rainstorm, I chanced upon a discovery of mind-boggling consequence for any wild turkey hunter. It had been another typical April opener: hoarfrost, high wind, and a sudden icy downpour. Pawing deep into a bed of wet leaves in the hope of finding a drier place to rest my haunches while the rain abated, I scraped against a rectangular object heavily encrusted with grime.

It proved to be a small spiral notebook, both the leather cover and the first several pages of which were reduced to a sodden pulp. The notebook's innards, however, were still quite legible.

Although both his name and institutional affiliation had been obliterated, the writer was clearly some sort of natural scientist, a field researcher working on what the neatly penned pages several times refer to as *Common Myths of the Woods*.

Much of his data refuting erroneous outdoor assumptions, it must be acknowledged, will be of interest only to the specialist. The first readable page, for example, begins: *"Myth #3: Woodticks breed primarily in the woods."* There follows a long section of tedious arcana, all simply to establish that the tick's preferred breeding grounds are fishermen's underwear.

Most hunters, I suspect, would find the notebook's next section equally uninspiring: *"Myth #4: The woodcock (timberdoodle) can fly vertically."*

Only the most apathetic outdoorsman, however, is likely to be indifferent to the notebook's final section, so astonishing are its disclosures. For this reason, and to ensure proper scientific objectivity, I shall from this point quote directly from the journal. Thus the researcher continues:

> *Myth #5: There exists such a bird as the "wild turkey."*
> This one has been around for decades, the bizarre springtime rituals of thousands of American males testifying to its potent allure.
>
> In its most virulent form, belief in the myth of the wild turkey triggers behavior almost manic in its irrationality: The victim leaps excitedly from his bed at three o'clock in the morning. He seems obsessed with clothing that bears the labels "Army Surplus" or "Camouflage." Grease-paint or charcoal are smeared over the face and hands. Front teeth are occasionally blackened. In especially acute cases—perhaps linked to transvestitism—the victim may squeeze his head into the leg of women's sepia-colored pantyhose.
>
> Such behavior is only the beginning. As Schwartz and Fuller have documented in their ongoing study, these oddities characterize but the first few minutes of "Turkey Season." The symptoms that follow are more severe.
>
> Though wildly varied, in the majority of cases they include at least the following: 1. The hunter wanders through the woods in a state suggesting both infantilism

and sexual arousal, cackling, hooting like an owl, rattling a small noisebox of the type sometimes seen suspended above infants' playpens. 2. Heavy breathing and other signs of stress mark acute levels of indecision. At such times, after sitting sphinxlike for up to an hour, the victim may suddenly rise and trot frantically across several ridge-tops, only to return some time later to the very site where he began. 3. In cases of particular intensity, the affliction abates at midmorning only to reappear with greater potency at sunset. Most commonly, the hunter will then be found isolated in his parked car on a logging trail or remote township roadway, hooting or rattling his box even more fervently than before. Questioned about such behavior, more than one victim has reliably been quoted as answering, "I'm putting a turkey to bed." Exhausted by the day's activities, he may subsequently nod off into prolonged slumber behind the steering wheel.

Such is the pathology commonly encountered in the spring. In the fall, the victim's behavior is, if anything, even more eccentric. Frenzied box-rattling remains in some cases a recurrent behavior pattern, though far more common is an activity for which no scientific terminology yet exists to replace the hunters' own expressive idiom: "Just let all holy hell break loose!"

In such cases—increasingly common throughout the mythical bird's supposed habitat—the hunter walks quietly through the woods until aroused by an unidentified bird's flutter or some other indeterminate noise. At that point he rushes headlong toward the sound as if in a state of demonic possession, hollering, cursing, shooting his gun maniacally in the air. Just as suddenly, he stops, finds a tree, and seats himself quietly in the lotus posture. He may

remain in such an attitude, as if awaiting cosmic enlighten-
ment, for a full hour or more.

In view of the above evidence and the dramatically
increased number of "turkey hunters" filling America's
woods every spring, a single conclusion appears justifiable:
The Myth of the Wild Turkey is approaching critical levels
of virulence. The compelling question is, What can be done?

Here, too, only one conclusion is possible: We must
publicize the *facts* so long obscured by the myth. Consis-
tent with Schwartz and Fuller's still unpublished findings,
my own research has validated the following:

The beginnings: November 19, 1953—A single domestic tom escapes from a truckload of market-bound
roasters owned by one Horton Bozerman of Keokuk, Iowa.
The lost turkey takes up residence in a roadside woodlot,
where he is photographed by an Ecuadoran tourist named
Jesus Jorgé. Never having seen such a bird in the less
exotic rain forests of his own country, Jorgé reports his
sighting at once to the International Audubon Society,
where through an error the turkey is eventually registered
as a previously undiscovered breed.

Unhappily, the lost tom does not live to see even
another twenty-four hours. Of pea-sized brain like all its
domestic kin, it is discovered early the following morning
still perched on the log where Jorgé sighted it, by one
Lloyd C. Fritzenbach. (Had the tom not almost immediately been disposed of in the Fritzenbach's Thanksgiving
festivities, Jorgé's error would certainly have been corrected through routine follow-up research.)

When the first of Jorgé's blurred photographs appears
six weeks later in *International Wildlife,* nothing remains

of the Keokuk tom but a single broken thighbone, mangled beyond recognition by the Fritzenbachs' Saint Bernard.

When others of the Jorgé photographs appear over the next few months in the mass-circulation outdoor magazines, the myth gathers momentum, substantiated in the popular imagination by an artist's rendering on a bottled whiskey of some repute. Inevitably, widespread "sightings" of the strange wattled bird commence to trickle in. The first (as is commonly known) are from Indianapolis and Yuma, Arizona. These are soon followed by a wave of others from scattered points throughout the continent. At last count the so-called "wild turkey" *(Gobleronious gallopavo)* has been sighted in all fifty states and is actively hunted in forty-seven.

Franklin's Folly and the "Flock" at Plymouth Rock: Notwithstanding the widespread. . . ."

Unfortunately, at this point the notebook pages become illegible.

And so the matter stands, at least until the researcher's identity is established. I for one see no reason to question his conclusions, though I'm of course aware that reported wild turkey sightings predate the seminal Keokuk tom by a good three centuries or more. (Can there be any doubt that it is precisely this aspect of the myth which is taken up in the notebook's unreadable final pages?)

I am also unpersuaded by the few "confirmed" kills that regularly appear at the end of every hunting season. Closer scrutiny will almost certainly prove them to result from the escape and slaughter of other hapless domestics, no doubt hyped by gullible DNR publicists blinded by the prospect of escalating license fees.

Casts of Thousands

THERE'S NO WAY TO SAY THIS DIPLOMATICALLY: America has too damned many fishermen. No one's home to spare the rod; "Gone fishing" means multitudes, not solitude. The last time I walked a stream that wasn't a beaten path, "gridlock" was a quote from Vince Lombardi.

If experience doesn't drive this truth home, statistics will. According to the U.S. Fish and Wildlife Service, last year over sixty million Americans went fishing, spending more than a billion man-hours in the process. (Mercifully, nobody seems to have tallied the figures on backlashed reels, hooked fingers, and sheared pins.)

Times are tough, in short, for anyone still clinging to images of the Isolated Angler frozen in midcast on the Big Two-Hearted River—a fact writ larger every time another hundred

yards of tangled monofilament from somebody's Pocket Fisherman gets snipped off and dropped on the sand. (Who could have
guessed, thirty years ago, what "standing in line" would come
to mean?)

What is to be done? Barring a federal moratorium on the
sale of nightcrawlers or a manufacturer's recall of Winnebago
campers, the possible solutions to our glut of fishermen, it
seems to me, have been reduced to two:

a. *"Tough Love" for the masses:* Taking our cue from recent
EPA warnings on polluted waters and fish teeming with PCBs,
we can intensify the campaign to make all Americans aware of
the innumerable risks of angling, especially in those southern
lakes and northern cold-water fisheries where water moccasins
and hypothermia are ever-present threats. Fish and Wildlife
statistics on angling-related bankruptcies, liquor consumption,
and divorce should be declassified. So should tackle-shop rec-
ords on over-the-counter sales of Dr. Juice.

Bumper stickers could contribute as well. In addition to
such gentle reminders as "Don't take a kid fishing today" and
"Fishermen make wetter lovers," I favor blunter messages: a
fly rod emblazoned "Just Say No!" for example, or bass lures
labeled "Don't Get Hooked!" and "Help Build a Plug-Free
America."

Actual conversion accounts of rehabilitated anglers have
even greater potential. Kids should learn early that for every Ed
Zern or Ernie Schwiebert there are dozens of surgeons and
CEOs who once used heavily out of the Orvis catalogue.

The message should be targeted at beginning anglers of all
ages, not just youngsters. Trout neophytes should be dosed
with data on tick infestation and the perils of Lyme Disease, for
example; novice bass fishermen should hear what chronic expo-
sure to Roland Martin can do to the organs of speech. Even

panfishermen may be reachable if approached at critical moments of self-doubt. Anyone heard muttering "Think they're ever gonna start hitting?" is an especially likely candidate.

b. If a Stop Angling campaign proved insufficient, I see no alternative but the adoption of the *Mandatory Fishing License Test.*

I realize the implications of what I'm proposing: more bureaucratic meddling with every American's right to gather nature's bounty. I can only argue, in defense, that big problems require big sacrifices. A proficiency exam would be a pain in the rear, granted, but so is being tested for a driver's license. Competency exams have been used for years in Europe as a means of identifying legitimate hunters. The Angler Proficiency Test, unfortunately, is simply an idea whose time has come.

Such an exam should cover the relevant terminology, equipment, and techniques of sportfishing in America. The questions should be basic enough that anyone with even a modest claim to the title "Angler" would comfortably pass. (The objective, remember, is to remove from our nation's waters the rod-bearing equivalent of reckless and drunken drivers, not to baptize a piscatorial elite.) For purposes of illustration, I offer the following rudimentary questions—one small example of the form a proficiency test might take.

1. Understanding Anglish: Part 1. Applying the standard Lost Fish Estimation Index, which bass described below is at least ten inches long?

   a. "He would've gone three pounds easy."
   b. "That sonofabuck was a good foot and a half if he was an inch."
   c. "Goddamn, boys, we had us a live one there."

2. In group distance-casting demonstrations, a leader with a heavy butt is a disadvantage only if:

   a. He also has short arms.
   b. You prefer the weight forward.
   c. It causes too much drag.

3. The Sofa Pillow is an especially effective fly if:

   a. You're fishing at night.
   b. Nothing's rising.
   c. The fish are on their spawning beds.

4. Surveys indicate that the average bait-shop owner:

   a. Knows what's working but won't tell you.
   b. Doesn't know what's working but will tell you.
   c. Would rather cut bait.

5. Most experts think which of the following usually works best for bass buggers?

   a. Hormone injections.
   b. Electro-shock treatments.
   c. Psychotherapy.

6. Understanding Anglish: Part 2. What is "Head Cement"?

   a. A hard-rock group.
   b. A fly-tier's tombstone.
   c. Official motto of the Army Corps of Engineers.

7. When a fisherman complains about the quality of his saddle hackle, he usually means:

a. His flies are riding too low in the water.
b. He's spent all day jockeying for position at his favorite pool.
c. He just lost a fish he tried to horse.

8. Some muskie fishermen swear they've fished all their lives and never had a strike. This proves:

a. Muskies are smart.
b. Muskies are rare.
c. Muskie fishermen would be rarer if they were smarter.

9. Which fish are notorious for their shameless love of "smutting"?

a. Chum salmon.
b. Grouper.
c. Trout who spend their lives working in film.

10. Among serious fly fishermen, the term "ultimate purist" is reserved for the angler who:

a. Uses only dry flies.
b. Uses only dry flies size 20 or smaller.
c. Uses only hookless dry flies specially tied for Non-Invasive Angling (also known as "lip service" or "touch and release").

11. What cinema classic depicts the tormented life of a South Carolina panfisherman?

    a. *Raging Bullhead.*
    b. *Porgies and Bass.*
    c. *Never Give a Sucker an Even Break.*

12. Caddis flies are said to be in the "pupal" stage when:

    a. They're learning how to swim.
    b. Trout take them in schools.
    c. It's May and they wish they were dun.

13. In its landmark decision on angler's rights, *Kreh vs. State of Pennsylvania,* the Supreme Court ruled unanimously that:

    a. A fisherman cannot be forced to sit at the end of a lunch counter, no matter how he smells.
    b. Mandatory IQ tests for ice fishermen are unconstitutional.
    c. "Inflating" a nightcrawler does not violate statutes banning indecent public acts.

14. Understanding Anglish: Part 3. A fish is said to be "fowl-hooked" if it's taken on:

    a. A hen-hackle fly.
    b. A rooster-tail spinner.
    c. An Eagle Claw.

15. Which of the following recent advancements in angling technology originated as a birth-control device?

a. Silicone line dressing.
b. The stream thermometer.
c. Neoprene waders.

Call of the Iceman

ICE FISHING. FOR YEARS THE TERM ITSELF STRUCK me as an oxymoron, one of those schizoid yokings that makes sense only if you're a surrealist, like *Los Angeles Laker* or *casual sex*. The fishing season flat ended in the fall, when fly lines gave way to duck blinds in the sane man's stream of consciousness. On those rare occasions when I thought about ice fishermen at all, they seemed as remote as the woolly mammoths, a hoary breed shambling over a frozen landscape somewhere in the Pleistocene.

Then I moved to Minnesota and got indoctrinated by the Geezer. I discovered I'd been right all along.

I first met the guy in a roadside tavern named Flippin' John's, one of those split-log sanctuaries whose neon lights beckon along every winter-bound North Woods highway. It was late November, with snow already piled so deep the mailman flew a caution flag from his CB antenna, and I had just skated a drafty van over fifty miles of glare ice down a tight corridor of pines. So preoccupied was I with simply working out the chilled muscle kinks that I didn't notice the old man squatting at the end of the bar until he spoke.

"Dat's real wedder out dere, hey."

At this point I should pause and be up front about something: Most of the previous winters of my life had been spent in southern Nebraska. That's not Acapulco, I know, or even southern Kansas. But it's a long way from Duluth. To put it bluntly, I hadn't adjusted to country where you start your car every morning with jumper cables and the kids set off to hunt Easter eggs pulling a sled.

The one thing I *had* learned for certain was how the natives hereabouts handle winter, something a newcomer better pick up quick or risk being labeled a wimp.

The native ignores it. Or more accurately, he adopts a posture that's best described as Northwoods Cool.

If it's the middle of May and you're playing the season's first round of golf on greens still frozen to the texture of sheet-rock, for example, your native simply gnaws a chapped lip and mutters matter-of-factly, "They're gonna play awful durned fast today, fellas." To which another native impassively adds, "Ain't holdin' worth a rat's ass, are they?"

From his oil-stained cap to the wood chips that flaked his Vikings windbreaker, the ruddy-faced old man at the bar gave every sign of being a native, and I steeled myself for the inevitable challenge ahead. I was damned if once again I'd be caught on the downside of a stoicism gap.

"Got a krick in your neck?" he asked, as I shrugged off my parka on a barstool.

"Nah. Just a little warm in here," I answered, tugging at the collar of my shirt.

"Yeah, dey think ever fisherman dat comes in off da ice is dyin' of hypodermia, but dat's a load of moose manure."

"That so?" It wasn't a topic I was eager to pursue.

The Geezer paused only long enough to bite off a chunk of Red Man. "Been over to da lake?" he mumbled, the chaw bulging in his cheek. "Dey been hittin' real good on waxies."

I hadn't been in the bar long enough for the snow to melt off my boot soles, and already the Geezer had me pinned like a blowdown grouse. Never having been ice fishing in my life, I figured I had two options: lie brazenly, or mutter something noncommittal in the faint hope he wouldn't catch the scent. Halfheartedly I went with the latter:

"Nah," I said, wiping my nose. "It's still a little early. I like to wait till things freeze up good and tight."

"Dat's a mistake, hey. Dat's a big mistake."

He looked at me over the tops of his glasses like someone who'd just discovered a stray hair in his jello. Then he arched an eyebrow and added, "You from around here?"

I flushed. Gave it up and told him outright I'd just moved into the old Benson place.

I should have lied. Within minutes he had me pinned again, insisting that I let him show me "how to do da job on dat lake." I countered with a half-dozen reasons why I couldn't make it. They had roughly the same effect as a few cockleburs on a German shorthair. In the end I grudgingly agreed to be ready the next morning when he came by to pick me up.

"Don't forget now, hey," he commanded as I headed toward the door. "Get yourself plenty of dem waxies in case for once da wedderman's right about it gettin' up to zero. Dey always hit like crazy when it's warm."

I was out of bed at seven, over an hour before we were to meet in front of the tavern, figuring I'd need at least that much time to get dressed. Through the ice-glazed kitchen window the sun was a congealed egg yolk perched on a fresh snowdrift.

I was into the second layer of insulated underwear when my wife appeared in her bathrobe.

"Let me guess," she said, shaking her head. "A reunion for old Pillsbury Doughboys."

Undaunted, I refilled my coffee cup and put on another layer.

"The Michelin man?"

I struggled into the blaze-orange snowmobile suit I'd bought after leaving the tavern, laced up my Sorels, and slipped on a pair of oversized mittens and a purple ski mask.

"No question—the backup goalie for Thunder Bay."

"Just don't turn off the electric blanket," I said, picking up my bucket of gear and filling the thermos with hot chocolate. "And leave the brandy on the shelf."

It was five miles to the big lake, and the Geezer drove it with his window open because the pickup's defroster was "on da fritzer." Unfortunately, the radio worked. Through the crackling static came word that the temperature was twelve below with a wind-chill of minus forty. The Geezer wasn't impressed.

"Dat always gets me," he croaked, "da big deal dey make about dat wind-shill. Who da hell tinks about wind when dere's *ice*?"

The road ended at the lakeshore, from where we could see

a tiny knot of fishermen out on the bay. Half a mile distant, they resembled a group of Arctic seals clustered around an airhole.

I was reaching glumly for the door handle when I realized the motor was still running and the Geezer's eyes again had that glinty look of a bird dog about to go on point.

"Wait here a minute," he said, hopping out without killing the engine. "Lemme take a good look at dat crust."

Grateful for both his caution and the few more blessed seconds I could huddle over the heater, I peered through the frosted glass as he stepped out onto the lake and began probing it with a heavy iron spud. Nothing could have been more reassuring. So what if a dozen other crackbrains had risked the long march across an unknown tundra. We obviously weren't going to venture out more than thirty or forty yards.

A half-minute later the Geezer returned, slammed the door enthusiastically, and gunned the engine. "By Got ve got lucky, hey. Dat ice is four or five inches at least." And with that he launched the pickup forward like a powerboat aimed at the horizon.

I'm not sure how long it was until I spoke. It was sometime after the Geezer convinced me to loosen my grip on his thigh.

"How deep . . . ?" I gasped.

"Da ice?"

"The water! The *water!*"

"I'd say about tirty feet, more or less, but I ain't no expert."

"Have you ever . . . broken through?"

"Nah. Dat don't happen dis late if you're careful. Coupla' years ago some guy drowned, but he was pullin' a stove out to his ice house. I been fishin' dis lake for fifty years, and dere's only twice dat I've even got da tires wet, bot' times close in to da shore. All you gotta do is kick it in da butt. Dere ain't no sense walkin' where you can drive."

At that moment a sound exploded under the pickup's wheels like the crack of a high-powered rifle, launching my left leg somewhere over the gearshift.

"Dat's a good sign, hey," he shouted. "Da ice is gettin' dat tickness dat makes it pop."

No one looked up as we rolled to a stop beside the other fishermen. Hunched on five-gallon buckets, they cradled their stubby rods like a group of aged orchestra conductors drowsing over their batons. Occasionally one of the rods fluttered a few inches upward, the only evidence of blood still moving through their veins.

It took about five minutes, most of which I spent fumbling with my mask and mittens, for the Geezer to haul out his auger and drill a few holes in the ice.

Five minutes more and he had both his jigging lines in the water, plus a tip-up rigged with a six-inch chub for pike. Using the frozen sausages that once were my fingers, I'd somehow managed in that time to knot on a tiny tear-drop jig. Its symbolism didn't escape me. The prospect of threading on a half-inch waxworm seemed more remote than a bonefish flat off Key West.

"Unless you got some met'od I ain't never heard of," the Geezer bellowed, waving me over to his bucket, "you gotta get dat line under da ice. Dem fish live in da water, hey." He returned my baited hook with a pointed homily on setting up rigs at home the night before.

I slunk back and let the stiff monofilament feed slowly bottomward through the icehole, then plopped down on my own bucket to wait.

I waited.

And waited.

I waited some more.

The few inches of line between the hole and my rod tip was strung with pearls of ice. Earlier, I'd begun jigging in a studied imitation of the Geezer's deliberate rhythm, a short bump every fifteen or twenty seconds. The tempo had gradually quickened down my shivering arms until the ice droplets clicked like worry beads. If fish would hit a jig suspended from a jackhammer, I was in great shape.

It suddenly struck me that the Geezer might appreciate a cup of hot chocolate.

Laboring, I rose off the bucket to the height permitted by my backbone, which had the curvature and flexibility of a ploughshare. I shuffled over to the Geezer like Peking Man.

There was ice on his eyebrows. Beside him lay a single small perch in the attitude of a crescent wrench, its gaping jaws frozen open in shock.

I asked him how long we'd been fishing. About twenty minutes, he mumbled. I didn't have the heart to ask if his watch might be suffering from frostbite.

"Want some hot chocolate?"

He reacted as if I'd offered him a flagon of crankcase oil.

"I never touch dat stuff, hey. Ya want a little antifreeze to take da edge off da wedder," he said, pulling a small flask from his pocket, "dere ain't nutting does da job like schnapps."

It took maybe fifteen minutes, but I gradually became convinced he was right.

I'm not entirely sure how long the Geezer kept me out there. Cold has a curious numbing effect on the cerebellum. I do know that at one point, sometime after I heard the faint wail of the village's one o'clock whistle, I wandered over to ask what seemed to me the painfully obvious question. Beside the Geezer's bucket, the stiffened corpses of two sunfish had joined the petrified perch.

"Abou'dimedogo?" I said, trying to sound nonchalant through lips that felt like frozen bagels.

The Geezer sat hunched over his icehole as if transfixed by some inscrutable truth. It wasn't until I shook him by the shoulder that he looked up, rubbing his eyes.

"It's a liddle slow today," he murmured, stretching his arms and yawning. "But dat's da ting, hey, dat keeps a guy comin' back. You never know when dere's gonna be one o' dem feedin' frenzies." He thought we should stay another hour "to give dem little suckers a chance to get off of dere behinds."

We did, and they didn't.

When he finally dropped me off at my car, the Geezer wanted to know where he could reach me. "Da next time, hey," he promised, "I'll show you what da *real* ice fishing is like."

I gave him a phone number. The guy's down the road whose dog bit me on the leg.

Large Mouths
and Shooting Stars

IT BEGAN WITH A VISION. AS HE EXPLAINED IT TO ME
some time later, his eyes shining behind the bifocals that mark
his twenty-five years as a public accountant, Floyd Will's first
glimpse of the epiphany came as Big Ideas so often appear to
men of genius—at the moment when things seem most dire.

In Floyd's case, that moment came as he lay bedridden on
his stomach from a heavy dose of poison ivy, the result of an
ill-timed call of nature during one of our outings on Winnebago
Creek. He had started scratching even before we cased our fly
rods, rode home with his hands scuttling like crabs between his
hoisted heels and his haunches, and wound up on the basement
hide-a-bed when his wife threatened to get him a motel room and
have his food delivered by Meals on Wheels.

It was a little after 2:00 A.M. in this "darkest night of my life as an angler," to use Floyd's own description of the incident, that the Idea swam into his ken. Silent messages were scrolling across the TV screen as an end-of-broadcast finale to *Mr. Ed* and *Let's Go Fishin'*, and Floyd faced the doleful prospect of untold sleepless hours with nothing to keep him company but his itch.

"It was such a simple message," Lucille wanly murmurs now. "Just a note asking for local-programming suggestions to fill the half-hour on Sunday after *The Crystal Church.*" But somehow Floyd's fuddled subconscious began percolating with celebrity fishing guides and a drawling horse.

By the time he was finally able to rise from his sickbed, Floyd was so far gone that Lucille barely recognized his voice. The only thing she could tell for certain was that he was feverish to fish again.

He called me a few minutes later, though even after he hung up I wasn't sure I'd just talked to the Floyd I'd hunted and fished with for years.

The old Floyd was as predictable as hair loss: a guy who had a single dry martini with his evening paper, kept back issues of *The Wall Street Journal* neatly stacked on shelves in his garage, and spent the better part of his annual two-week vacation visiting relatives in northern Iowa. That Floyd, the old Floyd, never walked a streambank armed with anything but what he unfailingly called his "net guarantee"—a half-dozen black Woolly Worms arranged by size on his woolpatch. Any other fly that a man might feel compelled to cast over the waters, he argued, was excess overhead.

But the Floyd I'd just talked to, or at least the guy who identified himself as Floyd and said he'd pick me up at seven on Saturday morning, was somebody new. This guy cackled like

Large Mouths and Shooting Stars

Walter Brennan after too much time in the desert, sprinkled his palaver with enough "Hooooboys" to make *Hee Haw* look highbrow, and ended almost every sentence by calling me "ole son." When I asked whether he wanted me to bring an ice cooler, he answered, "It don't make me no never mind, Bubba," and the only thing he asked me was whether I'd ever run a "videocam."

When he finally hung up, I had no idea what was going to appear on my doorstep Saturday morning, but it damned sure wasn't going to be the Floyd who once told me his lifetime ambition was to meet H. and R. Block. Still, I wasn't prepared for what showed up in my driveway. It was Floyd's Buick, all right, with its familiar old bumper sticker "Help reform tax reformers," but the rental boat it pulled might have come from a drug-runner's slip in Palm Beach. Floyd approached the doorstep in a long-billed baseball cap labeled "Woooo, PIGS, Soooey"—which bewildered me because I knew he'd never been south of Soldier Field, Chicago, in his life. He wore sunglasses I'd never seen, his teeth looked like they'd just been cleaned by a rock star's dentist, and his jacket carried so many logos he might have lifted it from A. J. Foyt.

"Ready to roll, ole son?" he said, mouthing a grass blade like a trail boss eyeing a wayward dogie. Speechless, I followed him to the car and climbed in. As we drove west out of town, I finally asked him where we were heading. "New place," he drawled. "I don't guess you ever been there. Fella' told me it's crawlin' with fish and ain't so big we cain't shoot the boat from the shoreline easy."

"What do you mean, 'shoot the boat'?" I asked, not sure I wanted to know. "Son," he answered, with the indulgent look of a fox who'd just found a way into the henhouse, "you and me are 'bout to join the ranks o' the rich and famous. We're gonna make us a demo tape for Channel Ten." And with that he turned up a pasture lane and parked next to a hoof-muddied farm pond about the size of a hockey rink.

It was probably a great-looking place if you were a thirsty Holstein, but as fishing water it had as much promise as your local sewage-treatment plant. Floyd, however, had a gleam in his eye I hadn't seen since the day he figured out how to make his goose decoys tax deductible.

He peered out at the pea-green water like a prospector eyeballing the mother lode. "Let's launch'er rat'cheer," he mumbled, jumping out and slapping the bow of the cruiser—a useful gesture since I didn't have the foggiest idea what he had said.

It took us over an hour of cranking and ratcheting to get the big boat in the water, by the end of which Floyd had clearly lost a tad of his former enthusiasm. But by the time we had the gear loaded and the motor purring he was revved up once again.

"I'm tellin' you *what*," he shouted, heading toward a few scraggly cattails. "Ain't this the most beautiful place you ever seen?" I was still weighing my answer when he killed the engine and began to rig up. Pawing through a technicolor assortment of crank baits, plastic worms, and "reed-runnin' spinner baits" that would have made the old Floyd blanch with tight-lipped dyspepsia, he tied on a small orange popper and handed me the videocam.

"It's time we got down to some serious fishin'," he drawled, loosening up his casting arm while proceeding to fill me in on "all the poop." If I got the gist of it, the plan consisted of me filming Floyd catching fish until his arm got so tired he couldn't lift it, at which point he'd shoot me doing the same thing. We'd take a few scenic shots of the boat from shore—he seemed convinced that through the cattails the pond would look like Okefenokee—and then "put a wrap" on the shooting with a skillet full of fish as a shoreline lunch. I told him I didn't see any shoreline that wasn't littered with piles of cowflop, but that didn't seem to faze Floyd. He said editing could do wonderful things.

In retrospect, I'll give Floyd credit for being right on one count: the place *was* crawling with fish. On his first cast the popper had no more hit the water than it disappeared in a splashy gurgle, which I managed to capture in all its resonance for posterity's eye and ear.

"Whooeee, I either got me a alligator or a big'un," Floyd cackled, holding the rod high above his cap brim. "Come on in here *son*!" I kept the camera rolling, and ten seconds later he boated a largemouth a good nine inches long.

The fish's size seemed to surprise Floyd a little, but he quickly released it and flicked the popper toward some submerged weeds twenty feet off the stern. Once more the hit came immediately, and this time the rod bent almost double.

"Dang, I got me the ole sow-girl for sure!" he shouted, swiveling in his boat seat. "Holy buckets, would you look at her shake that thang?"

Two minutes later he boated another nine-incher trailing about six feet of coontail.

This one he didn't raise high enough for me to shoot. Instead, he extracted the bass from the weeds under water and watched admiringly as it swam away. "Ain't that a beauty?" he murmured. "That's gotta be one of the—." Whatever he added got obliterated on the soundtrack by my coughing jag.

By the time I'd recovered enough to continue, Floyd was rummaging through his tackle box. "I got a feelin' it's about time to switch lures," he said, holding up a purple worm. "Hey, if you were a big bass and saw this rascal come adriftin' by your weedbed, wouldn't it pop your joystick?"

He made a looping cast toward the cattails and retrieved it without a strike, then had the same result on a second. I'd begun to reconsider my hunch that Floyd's wonderhole was really a halfway house for stunted bass, when he suddenly hooked another scrappy nine-incher. And then on successive casts he landed half a dozen more, all the same length, all looking as if they'd been cloned from the same spawn crop. To the camera's unblinking eye, it might have been the same fish being caught again and again.

After a few more successful casts Floyd threw down his rod and said some things you've probably never heard on *Outdoor America,* but it was clear he wasn't ready to pack it in.

"We ain't out here to measure 'em," he pronounced. "The never knowin's what makes it worth the goin'." Besides, he added, after hand-signaling me to turn off the camera, a man could do a lot with better camera angles than I'd managed to get so far. I told him *Angling with Floyd* might make a great title for the entire production, but he didn't seem to appreciate the suggestion. He hinted, in fact, that it was time for us to switch roles.

The size of the fish didn't change much after we swapped ends of the boat and equipment, but Floyd did manage to do some things with the camera I'd never seen anyone else perform. My favorite was the shot he got with his toes hooked under the gunwales, but the stuff he took on his back wedged between the boat seats was also pretty impressive, especially when you consider he got most of it with a bass dangling in his face. Somehow he managed to do it all without missing a beat:

"You check out the *size* o' that hooter?" he shouted at one point during the few seconds that elapsed between one of my hookups and the fish's surrender. "Look at that little-bitty ole spinner-bait you caught him on!" I didn't see much difference between the hooter and the lure that dangled from the large-mouth's small mouth, but by then I'd gotten educated enough not to point that out to Floyd.

Even so, it became pretty clear that in Floyd's eyes I wasn't showing a whole lot more promise as the fisherman than I'd demonstrated behind the camera. After about my tenth pygmy bass—which I'll confess to landing with somewhat less enthusiasm than I'd have shown for a cold beer and a lounge chair—Floyd suddenly stopped shooting and told me I flat had to get more involved.

"Goldang, boy," he grumbled, "you got to spark up a little if you're ever gonna get the hang o' this bid'ness. You ever hear anybody on *Fishin' Hole* say 'Think there's any chance we'll ever catch one any bigger?' And how often you heard Babe Winkelman ask, 'Do I got a fish on, or is it just my River Runt?'

"You get yourself a fish on that ole line," he added, jerking his arm skyward to illustrate, "all you gotta do is let those joy juices start to flow."

He took the rod from my hand and made a quick cast to continue the tutorial, and I'll be the first to admit that both the bass and Floyd were ready when they got their cues. The lure slapped down, the nine-incher struck, and Floyd picked up exactly where he'd left off an hour earlier. "Where ya goin', honey?" he crooned, pulling on the rod so hard that the fish tail-walked involuntarily across the water. "Shooooeebob! Don't this beat killin' snakes?"

We stayed out until Floyd had enough footage to fill a sizable chunk of Sunday morning, including some "mood shots" from the shoreline through the legs of watering cows. I never did get my part down to suit him. Our biggest problem seemed to be fish identification. It appeared to me that when all the shooting was over we'd bagged about fifty cigar-sized bass and a couple of bluegills with delusions of grandeur; what Floyd saw was a whole barnyard full of "hawgs," "ole water-walkin' sow-girls," and "goldanged studs."

I haven't seen much of Floyd lately. Channel 10 evidently didn't think the tape was quite ready for syndication, and Lucille says he's had to spend the last few weekends working in his office to pay the rental fee on the boat. She seems a little reluctant to discuss it. Floyd apparently tried to write the whole thing off as professional research, but the IRS disqualified him on some technicality.

Muddling

WHEN I WAS IN GRADE SCHOOL, ON THOSE DAYS THE teacher deemed too rainy to let us out on the playground at recess, we stayed inside for an exercise she called Pass It On. Seating the class in a circle, she instructed one of us to whisper a message to the scholar in the next chair. The words would then pass along, student by student, until they had gotten all the way back to the sender—hardly ever bearing any resemblance to what was uttered first. "Freddy loves Carla" would make the rounds and come back as "Big flies are eating Charley's peanut butter sandwich." "Dogs have ticks" would return as "Jennifer kisses toes."

At the time, Pass It On struck me as simply another of Mrs. Clutterbuck's devious abridgments of my constitutional right to get out and rowdy at recess. I wasn't clever enough to recognize that in fact she was offering a seminar in Muddle English. An Inward Bound crash course for the half-dozen of us who aspired to nothing more in life than to grow up as hunters and fishermen.

If I'd been brighter, I'd have grasped that Pass It On was Mrs. Clutterbuck's subtle way of passing on the distilled wisdom she'd gained through twenty years of living with Big Chuck Clutterbuck, her husband. (Big Chuck was officially a Repairman, but nobody I knew had ever seen him repair anything but leaks in his moldering duck boat. To his clutch of envious young admirers, what he really did was fish and hunt.)

In the several decades since, I've never met an outdoorsman who could explain the *why* of Muddle English, any more than Big Chuck and the guys he hunted and fished with could have explained why their verbal wires so often got crossed. "I'll pick you up at six" simply *becomes* "Meet me in the blind at five-thirty." Experienced outdoorsmen learn not to question the reasons why. The metamorphosis of "Leave the key under a front tire" to "Keep the key, I've got a spare" is probably something not even a linguist with the skills of a Mrs. Clutterbuck could illuminate.

The most you can hope for, if you're a hunter or fisherman, is stoic acceptance that such transmutations inevitably happen. The muddling is the message. To paraphrase the poet, "That is all ye know on earth about the way hunters and fishermen communicate, and all ye need to know." This truth probably won't console you much the first time you're waiting in the rain to be picked up by a buddy who's sitting in your car a mile downstream sipping Irish coffee, but give it time.

Like most outdoorsmen, I had to acquire this hard truth the hard way. The first lesson came the autumn after I'd passed from Mrs. Clutterbuck's classroom to the lower reaches of junior high. My friend Dexter called one chill Saturday morning and announced, "A big flock of mallards are on Bodger's Marsh. We could put a sneak on 'em. Wait fifteen minutes, then come in from the left." I grabbed my twenty-gauge, ran to the marsh, and executed a teeth-chattering squat crawl through swamp grass, muck, and bog water. It was the first stalk I'd ever made without spooking the prey—aside from sleeping dogs.

My heart pounding, I jumped up in wild-eyed anticipation of a sky full of greenheads. There weren't any. I looked to the right across the marsh. Dexter wasn't there, either.

When I got home my mother wouldn't let me in the house until she'd hosed me down and hung every stitch I was wearing on the clothesline. I couldn't talk to Dexter until she returned, holding her nose, and tossed my bathrobe on the frosted grass.

"Are you crazy?" he said when I finally got permission to come inside and call him. "I said they *were* on Bodger's Marsh. We coulda put a sneak on 'em, but they only waited around about fifteen minutes. Then they left."

A single field lesson in Muddle English should have been enough, but it wasn't. (I hadn't been one of Mrs. Clutterbuck's most attentive pupils, and it was easy to blame it all on the telephone.)

A few months later, Dexter grabbed my arm after school one afternoon and told me the perch were really hitting in Sam Gordie's sandpit. I agreed to meet him there at four, repeating the time and place to be sure there wouldn't be another foulup. He said he'd take care of the worms if I'd bring the sodas and candy.

I still don't know if perch will hit JuJubes after you've chummed them with M&Ms.

By the time I was grown and a college graduate, I'd had

countless additional lessons. They all reinforced what I should have learned years before in those sessions with Mrs. Clutter-buck.

A friend and I once backpacked half a day into a mountain stream for an overnight outing, for example, and set up camp beside the prettiest pool in creation. The tent was tight. The birch was stacked beside the fire ring. A pair of fat cutthroats lay next to the potatoes and onions on a damp fern bed. Rip took the skillet from his backpack and extended his free hand toward me.

"Give me the cooking oil and the matches," he said.

"Just take 'em out of your pack," I answered. "And grab the corkscrew while you're at it so I can open the chablis."

"You've got all that stuff, not me," he said. "In *your* pack. . . . With the cigars? . . . The *toilet paper?*"

We looked at each other as dawn slowly broke behind our eyelids. It was the trip where I learned how to extract shards of flint from bleeding fingers, and the way to make campground stew out of raw potatoes and a handful of cornmeal.

It usually takes an outdoorsman about twenty-five years to get fully educated in Muddle English. The process is yet another example of Nature's rhythms, an eternal cycle, like the seasons: most of us arrive at the wisdom of a Big Chuck Clutterbuck about the time our own kids are old enough to fish and hunt.

A recent experience with my ten-year-old offers a typical illustration. Naive sons become educated fathers with naive sons. I'd given him a spinning rod for his birthday and told him we'd go out on the lake around nine o'clock the following morning. Give the water a chance to warm up, I said.

It was still dark when I was launched from sleep by the point of a burglar's gun jabbed between my shoulders. Light-switched into babbling consciousness, I peered at the intruder hovering over the bed. He raised the rod tip. "Ready to go, Dad?" he asked.

We got out to the lake so early the fog hadn't lifted off the water. A cold drizzle had begun to fall. Stalling, I told the boy to put on his jacket and wait on the dock while I got the last load of gear from the car. When I returned two minutes later, the dock was empty. His jacket dangled from a piling. My voice cracking with anxiety, I shouted a homing cry through the fog.

"I'm right here, Dad," he said quietly, ten feet away on the boat seat. "Jeez, what's wrong?"

We headed for a nearby cove and rigged up with teardrop jigs for crappie and sunfish. "Just drop it over the side, then give it a little twitch," I said. "Like this." I was feeding out line to demonstrate when my hat flew off as if a gull had snatched it and went sailing toward the shoreline. A spinning reel whirred in accompaniment, then stopped dead.

"Dang it," he said. "Backlash."

We had another little lesson at that point. A psychologist would probably call it nonverbal communication. Five minutes later the drizzle turned to rain.

It kept on raining for the rest of the day and on into the following morning, a Monday. That night at the supper table I asked him how his day had gone.

"Rotten," he said. "Mrs. Panzerhoff wouldn't let us go out on the playground at recess. She made us play this really stupid game called Pass It On."

Coachmen

IT WAS A SATURDAY MORNING IN FEBRUARY WHEN the telephone rang as I was chipping ice off my doorstep. Dropping the shovel, I shucked my Sorels and padded inside to answer it.

"C'gradulations," the caller drawled. "You've just been picked by the Root Valley Reelmen. Fourth round of the 'naugural Cat Draft."

It took a second to recognize the voice.

"Floyd?" I said.

"You better believe it, ole buddy," he answered. "Get your tail on down here to draft headquarters so we can get a jump on this thing."

I didn't have any idea what he was talking about, of course. Ever since he'd gone off the deep end trying to become a TV fishing celebrity, I'd found it hard to get a handle on Floyd. There was only one thing I was sure of—he wasn't likely to take no for an answer. I resigned myself and carried on.

"Where are you calling from?" I asked. "Who are the Root Valley Reelmen?"

"Just get yourself on down here to The Gutter Bowl," he said. "We'll fill you in. When they write the book on trout fishing in America, you're gonna be on the cutting edge."

The snowplows still hadn't cleared the parking lot when I got to the bowling alley a half-hour later, so I parked on the street near the front door. Inside the lounge, Floyd sat at one of the booths with someone I'd never seen before. A tagboard chart was taped to the wall behind his head.

"Come on over here, Bubba," he shouted, as my eyes adjusted to the smoky light. "This big hooter's my assistant, Duke Dettle. We took him Number Two in the draft."

The stranger extracted himself from the booth and stood bulkily above me, his arms bulging from a "Reelmen" T-shirt like a pair of smokehouse hams.

"Makes you wonder who went Number One," I said, adding a smile lest the big hooter take offense. Behind me a bowling ball rumbled down the alley, then clunked against a single pin.

"Number one's me," Floyd finally offered, his cheeks reddening beneath his bifocals. "I founded both the league and the franchise, so I went *numero uno* myself. But hey, all that don't make no never mind. Let's start talkin' *trout*!"

"I'm confused," I answered. "What league are we talking about?"

"CATT," he said, stabbing his finger at the wall chart. "Competitive Anglers for Tournament Trout."

"You're planning to fish for trout in *competition?*" I said, raising my voice over the noisy wobble of a gutter ball. I wasn't sure I'd heard him right.

"You bet," he answered. "You gotta get tuned into the twentieth century, Bubba," he added. "Tournament fishin's what it's all about. I know it's your first day as a Reelman, but hey, don't you ever turn on your tube?"

"I've been shoveling snow," I said apologetically. "I've got a lot of snow over at my place."

"We got snow now, sure," he muttered, "just like ever' February. That means the season opener's only six weeks off. If we don't get started on some winter conditioning, Fox River's gonna kick our butt."

"Fox River?" I asked, even more bewildered at this mention of a tiny hamlet about ten miles up the valley road.

"You got it," he answered. "The Fox River Ferrule Dogs. Right now they're the league's only other franchise, so we're gonna see a lot of their rods come spring. Word is they throw a real tight line and get after you right from the get-go. And they know how to hit that open hole."

"I'm still confused," I said. "You're talking about fishing for *trout?*"

"Duke's checked 'em out. They're tougher 'n boiled owl, but that don't mean we're ready to call the hounds in. What I hear, they got some line problems, and their tackle's gettin' old. We go out there and fish like I think we can on the opener, we got 'em where the hair gets short."

"What do you mean," I interrupted, "they're the only other franchise?"

"Charter members," he said. "Just like us. We're workin' on another one up on Chicken Ridge, but it's gonna be awhile yet before the Hackleheads are ready. A man can't fish in this league just because he knows about line backing and what fly patterns are all about. It's got to *mean* something to be a Hacklehead or a Reelman." He stared at me as if I'd turned down a week in New Zealand for an hour of dunking doughballs for carp.

"It's probably great even if you're a Ferrule Dog," I added. "I just don't see what—."

"Listen up," he said. "It's simple. The only thing you gotta do between now and the season opener is get your legs in shape. You'll be our Number Four rod," he added, "after me and Duke and the old guy."

"The old guy?" I said.

"Right. He'll be down later for the slides. Duke says he's a little long in the tooth, but you gotta love the way he gets after 'em when he hits the water. He'll do us some good."

"What are the slides?"

"They're back in the film room," Floyd answered, twitching his shoulder toward a large broom closet. "The Duke's been out on Crooked Creek and got us some scoutin' shots. Come opening day, we'll have good reads on every hole."

"Are you serious about all this?" I asked. "What are the rules? How do you know who wins or loses?"

"Catch and release," he said. "Total inches wins. Polaroid validization. String-up on Bucksnort Bridge at the seven o'clock morning whistle. No fish scores unless you got a proof shot of him laid out flatside against a ruler. Fifteen-inch penalty for encroachment on another man's beat."

"Who decides where you fish?" I continued. "What if everybody heads for the Rockface Pool?"

He stared at me for a moment, then dropped his voice. "Speed, Bubba," he whispered. "It's the name of the game. Hit that hole first, it's yours."

"I don't know," I said. "Not too many guys run very well in hippers, and in April you can't wade wet."

"You got it," he said, winking. "That's the kind of thinkin' we're countin' on from the Ferrule Dogs. When we come out for that opening whistle, what's it gonna do to their want-to when they see us wearin' these?"

Glancing over his shoulder to be sure no one was watching, he reached under the table and pulled out a large box. Inside was a pair of brown neoprene waders. REELMEN was printed in orange block letters across the seat.

"You're going to wear those?" I asked.

"Where you been, Bubba?" he countered. "I swear, sometimes it's like you caught some train back to the nineteen-fifties. Don't you ever read your Orvis catalogue? You get yourself a pair of these things, you're gonna hit that hole a helluva lot quicker. I don't care if you have lost a step or two."

"I don't see how I can help you," I said. "All this is a whole lot different from the way I've always fished."

"You've got some work to do, sure," he answered. "Just like ever'body else in the preseason. I've got to start some weightin' work on my Woolly Worms myself. Don't worry about it. Duke's got it all down on your chart."

"My chart?"

"Sure. The poop, the stats—how you're gonna match up out there ever' Saturday, skillwise. Here, Duke can explain it. I've got to take a leak." He handed me his clipboard and shuffled across the carpet toward the men's room, shaking his head.

"Let's see what Coach's got," the Duke mumbled, taking the clipboard from me. "He's the one that did your scouting report."

"Coach?" I blurted, still awed at the bulge of the Duke's biceps. "You call Floyd 'Coach'?"

The Duke didn't say anything for a moment, chewing slowly on a plastic toothpick. Then he looked down at the clipboard and began to read.

"Let's start with your strengths," he began, "the stuff you can do to help us." He paused, glanced at my legs, then read on. "You've still got good wheels. Coach says you get to a hole about as quick after some other fisherman's left it as anybody he's ever seen."

"Floyd already told me that," I said.

"Okay," he said, looking up from his clipboard. "Let's move on to where you're weak." Blinking slowly and hunching what was either his neck or the beginning of his shoulders, he stared at me like a sea tortoise eyeing a crab. I didn't ask him if I had any other strengths.

"The first thing is how you handle the pressure," he went on. "The days when they're really hitting. Coach says you'll take the small ones for hours, but you hardly ever make that real big catch."

"The hard hits always surprise you," I admitted. "But over the years I've taken as many good ones as Floyd."

He paused for a moment, gnawing on his toothpick, then continued to read.

"Your fly patterns," he said. "They're stale. They're too dry, too predictable. Coach says you hardly ever go deep."

"What about Floyd?" I protested. "A weighted Woolly Worm is all he ever uses. He goes deep every time he picks up his rod."

The Duke looked up, slowly lifted a ballpoint pen from the table, and wrote "Attitude" on the clipboard beside my name.

"Gizzard," he went on. "Gizzardwise, you're just not gettin' the job done. You gotta get after 'em even on those days it's muddy or windy or your hands are numbin' up in the snow."

"I don't like to fish with pain," I confessed. "I head for home when I'm cold and hungry. Face it, I'm not the kind of guy the Reelmen can use."

"Guts it out," the Duke countered, biting down harder on his toothpick. "Even if you can't catch anything, we can always use you to block."

"Block?" I said.

"Right. Think about it. The Dogs'll have their eye on the Rockface Pool, but we use your speed to lock it up on the opening whistle. Then Coach and me and the old guy take over and really start to score."

"Wait a minute," I argued. "Is that the reason Floyd . . . ?"

"Hold on," he interrupted, "I think the old guy just got here. Looks like he just came in off the big lake."

I turned toward the door, where someone about five feet six stood in baggy wool pants and a dirty Vikings windbreaker, a checkered cap with earflaps perched on his slate-gray head.

"The *Geezer?* I said. "He's the old guy Floyd was talking about?"

"You know him?"

"I went out on the ice with him once," I said. "The Geezer's your Number Three pick? Floyd thinks the *Geezer* fishes flies?" I stared back toward the door in disbelief.

"Bait," the Duke answered. "Every team in the league gets one designated baiter. The old guy's old—no way you can get around it—but we're bettin' he can still get the job done, bait-wise." Hollering, he waved the Geezer over to our table. I tried to look nonchalant as he approached.

"Dem little sunnies are hittin', hey," he said, unzipping his jacket. "You boys oughta been out dere dis morning about six."

"I don't go out on the ice any more," the Duke responded. "Not since Coach taught me what fly fishing is all about."

"Dat's a mistake," the Geezer muttered. "Dat's a big mistake." He shook his head, then stared at me as he reached in his pocket for a chaw of Red Man. I pulled my collar up a little higher. He didn't seem to recognize my face.

"Here comes Coach," the Duke announced, as Floyd loped across the carpet toward us, his hand extended to welcome the latest addition to the team.

"Big guy!" he shouted. "Great to have you on the Reelmen. I got a feelin' you're gonna go out there and put some kind of numbers on the board."

The Geezer looked at Floyd like a man who's answered his doorbell expecting a pizza and found a Jehovah's Witness on the step.

"You're da guy dat called me dis morning when I was cleanin' fish?" he said.

"Good to meet ya," Floyd answered. "Duke tells me you're one pure-dee kind of garden hackler. He says watchin' you work the chub and crawler option beats rollin' doughnuts with a stick."

"I came down here for dat draft, hey," the Geezer announced, waving his arm in the general direction of the bar taps. "You said dis is where I'd meet da real men in da valley and get 'tree good rounds of brew."

"Brew? What brew?" Floyd said.

"I don't know, hey. Over da phone it sounded like 'Noggle Cat' draft, but dat's some new brand I ain't never heard of. Say, is all dis some trick, one of dem pyramid 'tings I been hearin' about lately?"

* * *

Floyd was still trying to explain it all to the Geezer when I saw my chance and ducked quietly out the side door.

"Hittin' that open hole, Bubba," I said to myself. "It's the name of the game."

Jaws

THERE'S NOTHING LIKE A COCKTAIL PARTY TO MAKE A fisherman start thinking about fishing. You know what I mean. After an awkward hour or two of stoic reflection on flow patterns and the preening instincts of the indigenous fauna, you finally position yourself at that coveted elbow between the canape tray and the bathroom. A gin and tonic as clear as the Henry's Fork in your hand, you figure you've done about the best a man can do to survive where prevailing is out of the question.

It's usually about this point that a Cruiser surfaces, jaw fixed on the nearest conversational hook, and says something on the order of "Carver tells me you're a fisherman. Pardon my bluntness, but I've always wondered, you know, why exactly it is that fishermen like to fish."

This is where it gets dicey. You can get only so much

mileage out of stream hydrology and the mysteries of the parabolic curve. True, there's always the Yahoo option—you can confess to being a barbarian whose pulse quickens at the mere thought of disemboweling a six-inch bluegill—but it will probably cost you any future acquaintance with Carver's season tickets or sailboat. All things considered, a stiff price to pay.

So what *can* you say?

If I had a pat answer, I'd be somebody's press secretary. The truth is, I've never known a fisherman caught in the choppy waters of cocktail Darwinism to escape with his ego intact. Most guys are grateful for the chance to drift goggle-eyed toward the bar ten minutes later battered but not belly up.

If a fisherman learns anything from the experience, it's the futility of explanation. A dissertation on the joys of angling is worse than a simple grunt or shrug.

Sadly, it's a lesson most fishermen have to learn the hard way, so strong is the impulse to explicate. Few things make one's own old scars twinge like watching some eager young zealot—scant moments earlier so full of himself, flattered to be asked the question—now floundering helplessly:

"Sport?" challenges the Cruiser, clamping down on a cocktail olive. "A ten-inch fish fighting for its life? That's your idea of sporting?"

". . . I release most of them," counters the struggling angler. "I, uh . . . I put almost every one of them back!"

"So it all comes to that in the end, does it?" (Slow, sad shake of the head.) "Sadism. The pleasure of inflicting pain."

The first rule of cocktail survival is never to let yourself get trapped in such an exposed position. Better by far the mote in the eye, the coughing jag, the hors d'oeuvre dropped clumsily on the carpet. Only if none of these suffices should you resort to the spoken word.

It should be brief, and cryptic. Your aim is self-preservation, not pontification. Low profile; no hackles. Strip the verbiage. Less is more.

But *what* words?

Ask ten party veterans and you're almost certain to come up with ten different patterns. I lean toward the existentialist arcane. The sage nod, a raised eyebrow, then the soft drop of a paraphrase from Sartre—with such light-line tactics even the most aggressive Cruiser can often be kept in check. The next time you're asked why you fish, drop something like a "dialectical immaterialism" gently into the backwash. Let it sit for a moment. Don't twitch. The take, when it comes, will be tentative:

"Dialectical what? Did you say dialectical *im*materialism?" (The heavy jaw drops; the high forehead furrows.)

"Right." (Profound pause, then a sip from your gin and tonic.) "Man" (pause) "nature" (pause) "post-Hegelian [sip] creative tension." (Large bite of smoked salmon; tongue worked meditatively over the molars.) "When you get down to basics, there's not a whole lot more to it than that."

Feel free to use it if it helps.

The offer is genuine, but probably pointless. As I said, the art of cocktail-party survival isn't the sort of thing fishermen seem able to acquire from other fishermen. If a mentor has any value, it's usually only in hindsight, his long-forgotten words of caution floating into your consciousness just after a Cruiser has left you for dead. "So *that's* what he meant," you say to yourself.

My own mentor, Big Chuck Clutterbuck, did his fishing back when outdoorsmen had yet to face the cocktail challenge. He wouldn't have known what to make of anybody dumb enough to ask him why he spent his life toting a shotgun or a casting rod. The only answer that would have made sense to Big Chuck, I suspect, is that old cliché, the Balance of Nature: you spend six months of the year hunting; then you fish for the other six.

Still, for all his small-town insularity, Big Chuck is the one fisherman I've ever known who might actually have prevailed at a cocktail party. He had the perfect qualifications: a bear-sized body and a minimalist soul. If still waters run deep, Big Chuck Clutterbuck was the Mariana Trench.

I was only thirteen when I learned just how low a profile he could carry. I had sought him out in his den to see if he could help me translate some difficult reading material I'd come across. Big Chuck was sprawled on his Laze-E-Boy, contemplating the sprung innards of an automatic fly reel. Spilled popcorn bloomed like wildflowers on the green shag carpet beneath his feet.

"Big Chuck," I said, approaching, stepping over a pile of grease-stained rags and a broken screwdriver.

"Yo."

"You busy?"

"Noop."

"I can't figure this out," I said, thrusting the last issue of *Outdoor Field o' Sport* toward him. It was opened to the small print in the back. "BREEDERS," the heading announced. A long series of what looked like newspaper personals followed.

"Lem'see," he said.

He dropped the reel on the floor and bent intently over the magazine. One oil-smudged finger moved slowly down the page.

"Quakars!!!" the first paragraph began. "Big-breasted double-cross chicks of bobwhite quail, mallard, and chukar! Nonmigratory, covey-trained, twice as prolific as sparrows! $9.99 while they last. Ernie's Exotic Birds, Tickfaw, Ky."

"Breeding Redworms!" said the second. "Pure Red-clay Georgia Stud and Dam. Walt's Worm Farm, Box 253, Baskerville, Ga. $6.95 includes postage and handling. Thoroughbred papers available on request."

The big finger moved on, its pace never varying.

"Witness Miraculous Birth!" read the third paragraph. "Only $8.49! Peckermeyer's Plastic Egg-Hatcher! Marvel at egg to adult metamorphosis. Peckermeyer's Bluebottle Fly Ranch, 42 Spratt Rd., Fluger, Ca. (Include $2 extra for Special Hamburger Habitat.)"

The finger slowed to a stop.

"Yup," he mumbled.

"Yup what?" I said.

The expression on his face mirrored the big walleye glued to a board above him. Fifteen or twenty seconds passed.

"What's it all mean?" I finally said.

"Whaddaya mean?"

"I mean, I don't know. . . . I don't get it. . . . What are they selling? And why are they selling them?"

Silence.

"They're selling something, aren't they?"

"Yup."

"What?"

He picked up the fly reel and began probing what was left of its innards with a pair of needle-nose pliers.

"Breeders," he said.

I'd probably still be in the dark if he hadn't kept the magazine and sent away for a dozen Quakars. They were kind of interesting to look at, but they sounded and smelled like hell.

Once or twice at parties since, pinned, when not even the existentialists were working, I've found myself imagining how Big Chuck Clutterbuck would have handled himself.

It's all purely speculative, of course. Even in his sunshine years, Big Chuck never got closer to a cocktail party than Super Sunday and a six-pack. No matter. Somehow, it still does the battered psyche good to envision him fielding the "Why fish?" question:

"Whats'at?" he begins.

"I was simply wondering—How does one put this?—about the curious appeal it seems to have for so many of you fellows. It's really quite extraordinary, don't you think? I mean, what is it you *find* out there?"

Seconds pass. Big Chuck stares blankly at the questioner. "Fish."

(Dry-throated laughter from the Cruiser; Big Chuck takes a slow pull from his Leinenkugel's.)

"No, seriously—jesting aside—why do you do it? You can *buy* fish. There must be something beyond mere provender."

(Pause of anticipation. Big Chuck scratches his ear.)

"Isn't there?"

"What?"

"Something deeper? Something more consequential than a few small fish that you fellows are after?"

"Yoop."

"What? What *is* it?"

(The Cruiser leans forward in anticipation. Big Chuck munches a handful of cashews.)

"Big fish," he says.

In the mind's eye the flight is swift but unremarked, a faint ripple across the party shallows. Big Chuck shrugs, then drifts nonchalantly toward the sideboard for another slice of turkey.

It's delicious.

Fame's a Lure

BECAUSE HE'S NEARLY ALWAYS A LOVER OF ISOLATION (the solitude of a quiet lake or distant river), the fisherman would appear to be the least egocentric of sportsmen. Not for him the public spotlight or backlit wall full of trophies in the basement den. Compared to, say, the big-game hunter or country-club golfer, the average angler in baggy pants and floppy hat would seem to care as much for renown as your local Roto Rooter man.

It's an illusion. Scratch a little deeper, and you'll discover that the fisherman lusts for Fame.

It's not the heady pop of flashbulbs or the press of an adoring crowd he itches after. The Fame that fills his dreams is of a totally different kind, reachable by two avenues only: 1. He can catch a world-record fish; 2. He can create a lure so memorable he lives forever in its name.

The first avenue is perhaps more accurately described as a rocky footpath. Only one fisherman rests atop each peak's summit, looking down on the struggling multitudes below. Even the word "rests" is something of a misnomer. With the possible exception of Henrik Henriksen, the Norwegian who sixty years ago landed an eighty-pound Atlantic salmon, no record holder's crown sits easy on his head. They all feel the hot breath of countless pretenders, every cast a new threat to their thrones. (Henrik would undoubtedly feel threatened too, were it not for a pair of mitigating circumstances: first, no one today can imagine an eighty-pound Atlantic salmon, let alone be deluded enough to think of actually taking one, and second, he's dead.)

That leaves the second approach—a lure that catches the eye of Posterity. Most anglers are smart enough to recognize that this avenue is considerably wider than the first. Make a fly or plug that catches on—another Royal Wulff or Herb Johnson Special—and you've hooked the skirts of Fame. Even better, given the fisherman's contempt for ostentation, it's a comfortably understated vanity. Long after you've gone the way of all flesh, anglers will be taking your name for granted every time they take your name in vain.

Another advantage of the second route to Fame is simply the odds. It's less chancy. The angler who sets his cap for a world record—sometimes at the expense of his youth, his job, and the family estate in the Hamptons—may be done in by the guy dangling a doughball off a dock with a ten-dollar rod from K-Mart. The official IGFA record book is littered with such accidents of fortune, as is evidenced by what's happened to the acronym. Standing literally for "International Game Fish Association," IGFA to a legion of frustrated record-chasers means only "I Got Famous by Accident."

Not that Fame is a whole lot less whimsical where the second path to glory is concerned. Anyone who has ever glanced at trout fishing's most famous fly, the Royal Coachman, is sure to grasp that fact. Sired by a peacock out of a Victorian haberdashery, it looks as likely to catch a trout as the swizzle stick in your next Polynesian cocktail. Yet it does. As a result, the Coachman is to the fame-seeking angler what the showgirl who wins a million-dollar lottery is to the housewife with some loose change in her apron. *Everybody*'s got a chance.

If this isn't sufficient inspiration, the aspiring plug- or fly-maker need look no further than his latest Cabela's catalogue, all the proof he'll ever need of Fame's capricious coronations: Stan Gibbs's Darter makes it big. The Marlin Brando sinks with scarcely a ripple. Millions of anglers every summer pay homage to Lefty's Deceiver. Roger's Fancy. Troth's Elk Hair Caddis. No one but his wife has ever heard of the Homer Circle Jerk Bug.

Thus enlightened, what is the fame-seeker's best tack when he sits down to tie or whittle his ticket to immortality?

It's safe to say his chances hinge on two primary considerations: the materials he uses, and the name he chooses for his lure. (To the inexperienced, it might seem as if the plug or fly's success at catching fish would prove paramount. This error is easily corrected through a day spent fishing with what's recommended by the owner of any tackle shop.)

Let's take a closer look at the two criteria:

A. *Materials:* Studying well-known lures leads the seeker to an eye-opening conclusion: there's no such thing as the "right" stuff. Anything works, from pubic hair to a tent stake. It all depends on what's handy when inspiration strikes. Sure, the Marlin Brando failed, but not because it was made out of black leather and denim. (The real reason, which had to do with the indistinct mumble it made when trolled at high speed through salt water, is too complicated to go into here.)

B. *Name:* In light of the freedom one thus has in his selection of materials, it should be clear by now that its name, above all else, is what determines a lure's success.

For the novice fame-seeker, this realization can be discouraging. His chances appear to hang on something beyond his control—the name he was born with. In a world of Lee Wulffs and Doug Swishers, what hope is there for a Harry Uhrenholdt?

An honest man could not argue that this conclusion is totally unwarranted. Rudy Zug's advantage when the time came to dub the Zug Bug is as obvious as a big hatch of Hexagenias. Before the fame-seeker junks his tying vise and settles into oblivion, however, he should be reminded of the Herb Johnsons, the Al Troths, the Weeb Woblrites. If the Hairy Mary makes it, why not the Hairy Uhrendholdt?

In any case, there remains an alternative for the angler with a hopelessly unresonant handle: he can go the route of the Muddler Minnow or Cop-E-Cat. This course, admittedly, doesn't offer quite the visceral satisfaction of a lure that carries one's actual moniker. There's nothing quite like riding toward Fame with your John Hancock tied securely to the hookshank. Coming up with a catchy nickname, nonetheless, gives you just as proprietary a claim to immortality. Is Tom Edison any less renowned than Thomas Crapper simply because he wasn't lucky enough to be born Thomas Current or Thomas Juice?

This secondary route to Fame, moreover, promises the same liberation noted earlier in the section on materials: anything goes. I for one could die almost as happy knowing the

Swedish Pimple was my legacy as knowing my name would be perpetuated by Al's Goldfish or the Heddon Vamp Spook.

If you don't carry the patrician lineage of an Adams, don't stop tying. Keep on plugging. A man could do worse than live forever as a Goofus Bug or a Rusty Rat.

Taking Care of Your Dear

FOR THE HUNTER, SOME THINGS JUST DON'T MIX—
they run against the grain of Nature. Rain and grouse, for instance, or a thirteen-year-old kid and a duck call. Then there's
your basic, well-organized deer camp and somebody of the opposite gender. It's not chauvinism. A man doesn't belong on any
basketball team where he's the only one wearing a jockstrap.
And a woman just flat doesn't fit in a camp where everybody else
is a man.

The intelligent hunter, I suspect, knows this intuitively, the
same way he knows not to bring along his dog or a bottle of
amaretto. Then there are guys like Burt Stoltz, who have to
learn it through the school of hard knocks.

To be fair, Burt didn't actually *bring* Erma Jean up to the
cabin. As his wife, she'd lived there almost as long as he had.

Still, a man gets used to certain patterns in his life, certain fixed natural rhythms. And to the five of us who for fifteen years had hunted Burt's woodlot the first weekend of every November, using the cabin was simply a *fact* of fall, like wood smoke or buck scrapes. I mean, it was only for three days. Erma Jean had always taken advantage of the chance to go visit her sister Rose in Omaha.

I should also add, in fairness to Erma Jean, that she was more than willing to vacate once again last November. It was Burt who balked at the air fare after Rose took the telecommunications job in Greece.

Her good intentions notwithstanding, there's no question Erma Jean's presence put a crimp in our Friday-night preparations, even after she retreated from the cigar smoke to her reading room upstairs. It was still hard to loosen up. Burt, particularly, seemed to be suffering from stress. It took him a godawful long time to get over the dryness in his windpipe, and you could tell every time he tilted back his head how wary he was about the situation upstairs.

Eventually, though, even Burt slipped into a few of the old familiar habits. He was actually the first one of us to forgo the comfort of the bathroom for the chill wind off the backyard deck. It definitely helped get the hunter juices flowing. We all agreed it never begins to feel like deer camp until you start sacrificing to Nature's harsher call.

Burt was also, if I remember correctly, the first to mention it was time we deodorized our clothing. For sure he was the one who pointed out we should do it in the living room or risk botching the job outdoors. The rest of us, of course, immediately saw his logic. You're almost certain to overuse Doe-in-Heat when you're sprinkling it on in the dark. I'm still confident in the long run we saved scent, even allowing for what Burt lost on the rug when he dropped the bottle. His little miscue might in fact have turned out to be a blessing in disguise. As he said, "It's always unlucky as hell if everything in camp goes perfect."

In any case, it was an easy error to correct. We simply picked up another bottle when we were in town the next day.

All things considered, the camp was running pretty well by the time we sat down to deal the first hand of poker—especially after Burt tiptoed upstairs and discovered that Erma Jean had apparently gone to bed. We were considerably relieved to hear it. Try as he might, even a careful hunter can't be sure that a woman won't disapprove of some little thing he's doing, and it was a comfort to learn we'd all adjusted well enough to keep Erma Jean from feeling any stress.

We had probably played for about an hour when Joe Kobuski stacked his chips and asked about the food situation. "Hey, Burt," he said, "you got anything around here to eat?" In years past we'd always drawn lots beforehand to pick the camp cook and provisioner, but with Erma Jean on our minds that ritual had somehow got overlooked. Fortunately, there's something about a deer camp that sharpens a man's ability to improvise, and through some creative work in the kitchen we made out okay. We might have lost a little of our guacamole when the cover came off the blender, but we salvaged everything off the ceiling and most of what stuck to the walls. We even made a second batch for Erma Jean to take to her Literary Guild meeting—more than enough, we all agreed, to replace the banana cream pie.

I didn't need any more food, but Joe and Burt said they were still hungry, blaming it on the feeding frenzy that usually hits the night before any opening day. Checking the cupboards, Norbert Lund grabbed a skillet and offered to make a bowl of popcorn. "Deal me in," he told us, "while I put on some oil."

In hindsight, it's easy to see now that he probably should have sat out at least while the oil was heating, as several of us pointed out while we were tossing baking soda on the stove fire. Even so, nobody blamed Norbert. You can't expect a man to fold his hand when he's sitting on a jack-high straight.

Because of the smoke, our game didn't last a whole lot longer, but nobody seemed to mind much. We'd gotten more interested anyway in Burt's argument with Spud Meeker over the best way to bugle up a moose. It was Burt's contention that nothing worked as well as a length of sun-dried pig's intestine, while Spud held out for the human voice. Burt finally dug out an old call he'd picked up for five bucks at a garage sale. Looking to the rest of us for confirmation, he tried to prove his point. Then Spud let rip with a bellow he said he'd learned on Loon Lake from a full-blooded Chippewa Indian. It worked, he said, only on animals with Boone and Crockett racks.

The rest of us talked it over and agreed it was damned near impossible to judge between them. Burt probably had a little more volume, but it also wasn't hard to conjure up the image of a big bull charging through the muskeg toward Spud's guttural grunts. Everything else being even, we finally decided the intestine would work better for any moose outside five miles, but for anything closer Spud probably had the edge.

Joe gave our traditional camp wake-up call by banging on an old set of antlers at four o'clock Saturday morning, but it took him a helluva lot longer than normal to rattle up Burt. "Just go ahead and eat without me, boys," he finally muttered, looking a little red-eyed from being rousted out so early. "I think I may have picked up a touch of some virus. I'll prob'ly feel better when you're done."

In the spirit of camp camaraderie the rest of us didn't force the issue, even though it definitely threw a hitch in our routine. I had barely started my second stack of pancakes, in fact, when Spud said it was time to finish dressing and head out to our stands. Because of the time we'd lost, we weren't able to do much tidying up in the kitchen, but we did manage to keep most of the baking soda from getting gummed around in the syrup Joe had spilled. It's not the way you like to leave a camp, but with Burt still in his bag there were extenuating circumstances. Thus it seemed only fair to let him handle the rest of the cleanup. He hadn't done any of the cooking, for one thing, and with his extra sleep he'd be a lot fresher when we all came in.

Because of Erma Jean's taking the whole upstairs, though, we ran into another problem just getting dressed and outfitted. When you're not only cramped but forced to hurry, it louses up even the simplest camp routine. In the end, we more or less agreed to wear whatever we could come up with from the pile of clothes and bedding on the carpet. Burt didn't crawl out of his sleeping bag until the rest of us had almost finished, so in retrospect he probably did get a little shortchanged. Still, in all honesty, there's not a one of us who wouldn't have sacrificed if we'd known what was coming. I'd even have given him his Gore Tex body snugs. It's simply that at that point we all figured, hey, with his k.p. duties Burt will be the first one back in off stand.

It's also a fact that none of us realized what had happened to the weather. The wind was blowing like hell, and the temperature must have dropped twenty-five degrees since my last trip out on deck the night before. You could tell right away no deer were going to be moving unless they had some polar bear in their genes.

Still, I stuck it out. It was only when I couldn't see through the ice glaze on my eyeballs that I finally climbed out of my tree.

It was a quarter after seven. Joe and Spud were already back, along with Norbert, huddled in the front seat of his car with the heater cranked up to high. Dropping my gun, I climbed in the rear.

"Where's Burt?" I said, hunching forward to get closer to the dashboard.

Nobody answered.

"I'll give him credit," Joe finally said. "That sucker's a lot tougher than I thought he was. Stayin' out this long on stand."

"How come you're not in the cabin?" I said. "You know, that place with the stove and coffee?"

This time nobody broke the silence until I'd begun to wonder if I should check for carbon monoxide. "Door's locked," Spud mumbled. "Erma Jean must have gone into town."

It was probably about five minutes later when we heard the unmistakable high-pitched whine of a chain saw up in the wood-lot. And about ten minutes after that we saw a blue snowmobile suit moving through the aspen and figured Burt was finally coming in.

Then Spud said, "Wait a minute. Burt was wearing blaze orange." Then Norbert said, "Right, and that guy just don't walk like Burt. He's shorter, for one thing, and look how he's jutting out his chin." But then Joe said, "I don't know—that sure looks like Burt's hat, and he's heading straight for the cabin."

It wasn't until after she dropped the saw and slammed the door behind her that anybody spoke again. "Pretty late to be cuttin' firewood," Norbert said.

We all went back out to check on him, of course, even though we weren't warm yet. Burt was still sitting up in his tree—he had real good height to see deer from—but all the branches had been sawed off beneath. In the wind it was hard to tell exactly what he was shouting, but from the way he was waving his arms we figured he was ready to call it quits. He didn't have enough clothes on, for one thing. And as Norbert said, "Your odds drop like hell whenever somebody's been out cuttin' with a chain saw, I don't give a damn what kind of a stand you're in."

Hard as we tried, though, we couldn't figure a way to get him down. After about an hour we finally went back to the car where it was easier to concentrate. That probably seems a little callous—leaving Burt up there swaying in the wind like some big neon Christmas ornament—but it had to be done. There wasn't any way to help him if we stayed.

Besides, back in the car it didn't take more than thirty minutes before Spud came up with a solution. "Keenie Johnson!" he shouted. "He's a roofer. If we can borrow his ladder we'll have Burt down in nothing flat."

Unfortunately, it turned out to be one of those instances when the execution fell a little bit shy of the engineering. There wasn't any problem with Keenie, at least not after we convinced him Burt was up too high to jump, but we couldn't find a way to haul the ladder on Norbert's Chevy. We finally had to make a trip into town to bolt on Spud's canoe racks.

It was the kind of experience that puts a considerable strain on any man unlucky enough to have to handle it. We all figure Burt owes us at least a steak dinner for the aggravation he caused. Not to mention the embarrassment. It feels downright ridiculous walking through the woods with a thirty-foot extension ladder on your back. Then there's the obvious fact that while we did all the work, Burt got to keep on hunting.

Add to all this the knowledge that it took us until almost noon—close to eight hours without eating—and you'll understand why we were all a mite testy by the time we finally got back to Burt's pine. He was still up in his stand, of course, like some pirate scanning the horizon from the crow's nest, and it took him the devil's own time to climb down. I've never seen an able-bodied man who looked more like he needed to do some serious stretching exercises.

But we waited. In fact, it wasn't until Burt was finally on the ground, looking kind of wild-eyed, that Norbert asked him the obvious question.

"See anything?"

Ways of the Watchmen

A FEW OF US WERE SITTING AROUND FLIPPIN' JOHN'S
a while back, talking shotguns and harebrained shorthairs, when
somebody raised the question that always seems to surface
when such a wildlife seminar gets down to the real conundrums.

"What's the mark of a true hunter?" is the way it was put
on this occasion, if I remember correctly, though you'll no doubt
recall other variations from your own deer camps and Dew Drop
Inns: "What's a hunter's ultimate test?" "Do we still have rites
of passage?" "What's the difference between a real hunter and
the guy who's simply out walking through the woods with a
gun?" Etc., etc.

There are hundreds of possible answers, of course, from
one's first wingshot grouse to escaping a charging grizzly. My
own favorite is probably the one I heard in a Wyoming hash

house from an old mossback still hauling bull elk out of the mountains at seventy-five. "The real hunter," he mumbled through a mouthful of syrup-drenched eggs and buttermilk pancakes, "is anybody smart enough to track a mountain goat and dumb enough to try."

It's a question that's been around from at least the time the first portrait painter put a guy with paws and antlers on his cave wall. And I'm not deluded enough to think the answer I'm about to propose will silence many future campfire debates. Still, I'll offer it as one man's field-tested opinion on the surest way to weed out the mere gun-toters from the genuine article: What marks the true hunter has less to do with killing game than with killing time.

Think about it for a minute, remembering your own experiences as a hunter. Haven't there been days when your game bag wound up full, irrespective of skill or strategy? Days when the same success would have come to anybody who could shoot a lick, from a sap to a stumblebum? But how many times, before you became a *hunter,* were you able to stay planted in a duck blind when nothing but clouds moved in the frigid sky for hours—suppressing the urge to check out whatever it was that dipped low over that reedy backwater at dawn?

To my mind, at whatever moment you developed this kind of sit-and-wait forbearance, it was only then that you became a genuine hunter, a master at the art of killing time.

I say all this assuming nobody whose brain doesn't require watering is capable of surviving the average day in a duck blind or deer stand *without* having learned this ancient art.

Fortunately, most of us come to the gun under the tutelage of those who have sat, or stood, this sphinxlike course before us: fathers and grandfathers, most commonly, Zen masters at the art of killing time. My own apprenticeship was served through many a duckless morning in the 1950s on the barren flats of western Nebraska, when a "big flight" meant anything more than a wayward merganser and an occasional passel of greenwing teal.

In such times, you either learn how to kill time or you stop hunting altogether. Not entirely by choice—and mostly from absorbing the unspoken rituals of my elders—I eventually learned to do the former.

How the novice learns this depends on what and where he hunts. In my case, the first step was coming to appreciate how a good duck blind is constructed—"good" in this case meaning more or less the opposite of what the term means when applied to all other structures built by man. Nobody would prefer a house with a mud floor, for example, to one made of wooden planks. Yet to the experienced time-killer, the advantage of the mud or sand-floored duck blind is obvious; it affords endless opportunities at trenching and backfilling with his wadered feet.

The best blinds, I came to see, are those with a single plank bench from which the seated hunter can gouge and tunnel for hours, his leg working up and down through the mud or sand like the rocker beam on a good oil well. On particularly slow days, in fact, especially when flanked by another veteran hunter, I've left blinds at sunset that looked as if two hostile colonies of moles had settled into a state of prolonged trench war.

In one of those countless little cruelties Nature has somehow seen fit to visit on the beleaguered waterfowler, however, both mud and wet sand eventually freeze. There inevitably comes that first ice-bound morning when all heel-work halts with teeth-rattling finality. Such a day will test the hunter heart in even the most dogged trencherman, forcing him to try other ways of countering the relentless stoppage of time.

Whittling is one possibility, if your blind is made out of

wood or willows, though the same weather that has forced you to it in the first place usually aborts the attempt after little more than a few sluggish ticks of your watch. Frostbite makes it hard to handle a knife, for one thing, and doing it in mittens only works if you don't mind a few of the notches winding up on your thumb.

Another option is to fuse, stuff, or creatively mutilate the blind's assortment of spent shell casings, though this form of wildlife art depends on *somebody* ahead of you having had the kind of day when it wasn't necessary to kill much time. It's also not likely to carry you much beyond the morning's second or third cup of coffee. Even in the age of three-inch magnums, there are only so many things you can do with a shotgun shell.

That leaves the one creative time-killer that, year in and year out, has probably saved more waterfowlers from permanent brain damage than anything except the magic fluting of mallards—the blind log. Here, for nothing more than the cost of a pencil and a cheap drugstore notebook, the aspiring hunter learns just how much his forebears have to teach him about the quiet art of killing time.

I'm not sure why, but most of the good logs I've seen have come from goose pits around the country. It may be because geese fill the November sky even less often than ducks do. Or maybe waiting for a web-footed bird to descend on cornstalks simply calls for more imagination than gazing out at a flowing stream. With the river, you've at least got an outside chance something worthwhile might eventually drift by—a lonesome duck, a loose decoy, a piece of furniture from somebody's swamped houseboat. In a goose pit, it's a lot harder to convince yourself anything you'd likely want to keep is going to come tumbling out of the sky.

There's also the fact that most pits are heated, making it easier to write.

Whatever the reasons, when it comes to the kind of seasoned time-killing that separates the real veteran from the guy who's simply doodling with a ballpoint, the goose-pit log is tough to match. Take the following excerpt from an old log I came across a while back in a pit in North Dakota. It probably won't strike anybody who's never hunted as Pulitzer Prize–winning material, but to my mind it's damn near inspired:

"Got here 6 A.M. Cooked breakfast (2 eggs, 4 strips of bacon, coffee). Set out decoys. Nice sunrise. Nothing flying. 8 A.M.—ate mid-morning snack (3 eggs, 6 strips of bacon, 1 Milky Way, coffee). Nothing flying. Thought birds would decoy better so moved set from west to east. 10:30—ate lunch (mooseburger with onion, Pepsi, bag of potato chips, jellybeans). Nothing flying. Set out snow-goose profiles found in gunny-sack behind bench. Changed decoy set from east to west. 1:07 P.M.—mid-afternoon snack (rest of eggs, 2 Milky Ways, rest of coffee). 1:46 P.M.—saw single bird on south horizon, slow and high. Cawed like crow but looked like goose. 2:11 P.M.—felt sweat under hatbrim. Afraid food would spoil so finished what was left (rest of mooseburger, rest of bacon, 3 Milky Ways, small box of doughnuts). 4:00—hungry as hell, didn't bring enough provisions. Sunset—picked up decoys; pair of Canadas came in low, wings set over profiles. Gun left in blind, wrenched right knee diving for it across food-box. 5:32 P.M.—heading home (cased gun should work as crutch, tore up longjohn bottoms for knee-brace). Pair sign tomorrow could be big day."

Yet for all its challenges, the goose pit isn't the ultimate test for the man who would consider himself a hunter. And as most veteran watchmen will emphatically tell you, it's not likely to attain that status anytime soon. Not as long, at least, as a single deer stand remains in the woods. For it is here—in a tree, alone, his haunches numbed on a scrap of lumber—that a man learns how truly tough a critter Time can be to kill.

Nothing that follows will make it a whole lot easier. The truth is, even our wisest forebears fail us here. None of them has passed along anything that comes close to doing for the guy with a deer tag what trenching or log-keeping does for the hunter of waterfowl.

In the absence of such tradition, most of the stand-sitters I know have been forced to go it entirely on their own, improvising as best they're able. One or two count squirrels. A few have become connoisseurs of leaf patterns and the diseases afflicting tree bark. Still others ponder those ancient quadratic equations the how-to articles never seem to cover, like the one involving altitude, a full bladder, and telltale scent. I even know one guy who brings along the tax tables and works on itemizing his deductions whenever he's up in his oak.

Tactics bred of desperation, obviously. With results that are chancy at best. Last fall the guy with the tax guide, for example, let a wall-hanger whitetail slip past him while he was trying to get a fix on what insider trading is all about.

There are, I suppose, a few basic training exercises that might make the long hours of tree-perching a little easier— watching *Donahue,* for instance, or raising a tankful of clams. But in the end, an honest man has to acknowledge that the only sure-fire time-killer in a deer stand is killing a deer.

The Other Side

"JUST LIKE I SAID FROM THE BEGINNING," NORBERT Lund grumbled. "It's too goldanged late in the year to fish."

Rising stiffly, he hobbled across the rough plank floor of the cabin. Pulling a log from the woodbox, he struggled to turn the creaking handle of the barrel-belly stove. No one moved to help.

"The wind's got to stop blowing sometime," Joe Kobuski finally offered, his voice barely audible above the tamaracks groaning over the rooftop.

"Right," Burt Stoltz said. "And Erma Jean's gonna show up with the other women any minute. She's gonna say they all changed their minds and we can use the house for a deer camp just like ever' other year."

Again no one spoke. I resumed staring out the cabin's

single window. Wet snowflakes splatted against the cracked pane like drunken moths.

The door opened suddenly to a blast of Arctic air, followed by the hunched, bundled form of Spud Meeker. He set a bucket of water down by the battered pots and pans stacked in an orange crate next to the rust-stained sink.

"Can't be more than half a mile to the outhouse," he said. "And nothing's wrong with the pump but a broken handle. It works great after you've hauled a few gallons up from the river to prime it with." He eyed me the way a librarian does when you return a book with a coffee stain on the cover. Behind him, the stove labored feebly against the wind whistling through the thin clapboard walls.

"It's only costing us eighty bucks for the weekend," I said defensively. "Since it's the deer opener, I got the guy to come down quite a bit." The words hung in the air like stove ash.

Norbert shook his head. "The opener," he muttered. "First one I've missed in thirty-two years." He peered gloomily at the fire through the smudged isinglass.

"I never missed one since I was ten," Burt mumbled.

"Twenty-eight for me," Spud added, water puddling at his feet from his wet gloves and parka. "Not counting the year I had the hemorrhoid operation."

"I thought you even made that one," Joe said. "Wasn't that the year we brought the cushion and hoisted you up to your tree with a forty-foot rope and a truck tire?"

"That's right," Burt said. "I remember it 'cause I strained my back getting him down. Spud and his hemorrhoids. It was the same year he slept all night on the bathroom floor."

"When Norbert tripped over him in the dark," Joe added.

"And snapped off the shower curtain."

"Different year," Spud said, shaking his head. "You're talkin' about 'seventy-five, when I had that boil they had to lance in the hospital. It was the same year Joe got lost tracking the six-hundred-pound buck."

"That turned out to be one of Al Welby's shorthorns," Burt said.

"I wasn't lost," Joe protested. "And his tracks looked just like Old Shadrack's."

"You weren't lost," Norbert said, "when you called us up from Al's house at midnight."

"And Old Shadrack did look a lot like a steer," Burt added, "the time I saw him feeding up in my meadow."

Outside, a limb popped in the wind and crashed down a few feet from the woodpile. No one else in the room got up to look.

"I still can't understand how he got by you in 'seventy-eight," Joe said to Norbert, "even if your mittens did get caught in your zipper. He couldn't have been more than fifty yards from your tree."

"First of all, it wasn't 'seventy-eight," Norbert mumbled. "'Seventy-eight was the year Burt grabbed the wrong box of shells and got three good shots at him with grouse loads."

"They weren't good shots," Burt protested. "He was in the aspens and moving left to right."

"Second of all," Norbert continued, "it was my underwear, not my mittens. He slipped past me in the brush."

"I don't know," Burt said, pulling another log from the woodbox. "I think Joe's right about it being 'seventy-eight. It was the same year I gave Erma Jean the rototiller on her birthday."

"For her flower garden, wasn't it?" Joe said.

"Right. I remember it because when mine rolled around she gave me those two plane tickets to Mexico City. I spent the last four days of the season listening to mariachi bands."

He nudged the log into place with a bent tire iron, waited till it flamed, then clanked the door closed and turned toward the table. Opening a can of tomato soup with his knife, he poured it in a pan and added a cup of water. He put a lid on the pan and set it on the stove to boil.

"When'd you learn how to cook?" Spud said.

"After Erma Jean started her pottery business. Mondays and Wednesdays I do all the meals, Friday nights I just do dinner. It's not that bad once you get used to it. Tacos is the only tough thing I ever make."

Joe rose from his cot and brushed past me to peer into the woods outside the window. "What do you think they're all doin' right now?" he asked. "You think they're actually up in the stands?"

"I doubt it," Burt said. "It's way too cold, for one thing. Erma Jean said they might use 'em for an hour or two if it was sunny. Otherwise they were gonna rent some movies and a VCR. I think they also plan to discuss a book."

The soup pan began to rattle, its pink contents bubbling over and running down the sides. Burt fumbled in the drawer for a pot holder and lifted what was left of the soup off the burner. Pouring it into five chipped cups, he motioned us toward the table. Stools scraped awkwardly against the floor as we sat.

"I guess it's only fair," Spud said, tearing the top off a box of crackers. "We've used it for the opener ever since you bought the place."

"I don't know," Norbert objected. "I still say it never would've come to this if it hadn't been for that Christmas present. If Burt hadn't given her that Browning automatic, we'd be sittin' up in those stands right now ourselves."

"Hindsight," Burt protested. "It's always twenty-twenty. If you knew your wife was gonna give you an exer-cycle, what would you've done?"

"But readin' books and watchin' *movies*!" Norbert shook his head. "I'll bet they didn't even roll out of bed until nine or nine-thirty. You call that hunting deer?"

"I don't think that's what they're calling it either," Burt said. " 'Consciousness raising' is what it's all about."

"But there ain't nothing wrong with my conscience!" Norbert shouted. "My goldanged conscience is raised as high as it's ever gonna get!"

For a minute or two the only sound was the slurp of soup and the snap and crunch of crackers. Snow continued to fall in fat flakes, but the wind had begun to die down.

"They prob'ly don't even care if they get one," Norbert grumbled. "I'll bet Son of Shadrack could walk right by that big living-room window and they wouldn't even load their guns."

Again no one spoke. Finally Burt got up and cleared the cups from the soup-stained table. He stacked them precariously in the sink, then sat back on his stool.

"I wonder if Son of Shadrack's still out there," I said. "It's been a long time since anybody's seen him."

"He's out there," Norbert said. "Put me up in the Crab-apple Stand tomorrow morning and I'd give you even money he'd come down the Cedar Trail."

"The way he did in 'eighty-five?" Burt asked. "When you were eating the chicken sandwich?"

"It was 'eighty-four," Norbert said, "and it was a ham and cheese on rye. I could've shot anyway, but he was heading straight up the spruce ridge toward Spud."

"If that was Son of Shadrack," Spud said, "he took some

horn-shrink pills during the summer. The deer I saw wouldn't have gone ten points if you counted his hooves and tail."

"Was he the one that spooked when you dropped your thermos?" Joe asked. "Or the one you missed because of the bluejays?"

"Starlings," Spud corrected. "It was the biggest bunch o' starlings you ever saw."

"I hope some of 'em were around this morning," Burt said, "if Erma Jean got out with her binoculars and birdseed. She said they all agreed they'd rather see birds than deer."

The cabin went still except for the muffled echoes of Norbert groaning. It was the sound of a man who's just discovered what the new puppy he left in the back seat has done to the upholstery in his car.

"Birdseed?" he moaned. "They're using the stands for watchin' *birds*?"

"Birds and squirrels," said Burt. "Erma Jean bought some nuts they were gonna take along with 'em. She said she's wondered if squirrels would come to nuts ever since the year I told her about the one that ran up Joe's leg."

"When he fell asleep in the Oak Stand?" I said.

"And Shadrack ran right under him chasing the doe?"

"I wasn't asleep," Joe said. "I was resting my eyes from sun glare."

Norbert groaned again and walked to the cabin window, where the paler light of evening had begun to filter through the trees. "I gotta do something," he said. "I can't take this any more."

The rest of us slouched at the table. Burt's fingers drummed quietly on the wood.

"I'll even fish," Norbert said.

We looked at each other, then back at Norbert, who had sat

down on a cot by the wall. His eyes were watery, and his face was grizzled. Tufts of gray hair poked out from beneath his cap.

"The wind's died," Joe said.

"And we've still got about an hour of daylight," Burt added.

"Why not?" Spud said.

We pulled rods and spinning reels from the pile of gear stacked behind our sleeping bags and rigged up inside the cabin. Then we slipped on hip boots and headed down the trail toward the stream.

"It's supposed to be good here for northerns," I said. "The guy told me the colder the weather gets the better it is."

"Then why isn't he fishing?" said Norbert.

I had to tell him he was hunting deer.

Spud led us down the trail. The river glinted pewter gray below us through the still pine and balsam. The wind had died, but the snow was falling thicker—big goosedown flakes that hit the water like tiny parachutes and disappeared.

We stood on the shoreline holding our rods, staring at the quiet river. The only sounds were the frigid music of the water and the sharp, offset rhythms of our breath.

It was then, on the other side, that the buck stepped out of the alders. He raised his head languidly and stared down the river at us, the tines rising in an ivory thicket above his ears.

Seconds passed, and the deer didn't move, his right foot poised over an ice shelf, our rod tips tilted upstream toward where he stood.

Then Norbert raised his arm and flicked his spinner in a long looping arc toward the whitetail, which was gone before the silver blades hit the water two feet from where he'd stood.

"Nuts," Norbert said.

When the Going Gets Tough

BEFORE I GET INTO THE HARDSHIP TEST AND ITS ORI-
gins on Loon Lake during a driving rainstorm, you need to know
a few things about Clayton Stumpf. It will give you a better idea
of what the test is all about, for one thing, and it might even
improve your score. I should also tell you that Clayton hasn't
yet located the answers to any of the questions. He says nobody
should need them if he's spent any time at all outdoors.

Clayton wouldn't impress you much if you saw him from
shore squatting on his unpadded boat seat. And he's never going
to rival Lee Wulff as a fountain of angling lore. But to anybody
who has sat across the thwarts from one of his dog-day rumina-
tions, Clayton's mark of distinction is obvious: The man is im-
pervious to pain.

Okay, so you also hunt and fish with guys who consider

themselves barometers of outdoor hardship. You may even think you're a pretty fair yardstick of sporting affliction yourself. No matter. We're talking ultimates here. What sets Clayton apart is that absolutely nothing moves him to complain. Whatever you've previously thought of as the outer limit of the overused term "pain threshold," Clayton Stumpf would stretch it. If the Fates had seen fit to set him down in the middle of the Little Bighorn, he'd have turned to Custer and muttered, "You think *this* is bad?"

But back to that waterlogged afternoon out on Loon Lake. I'd worked my way through a soggy bagful of what was either runny fudge or a liquid peanut butter sandwich, when I made the mistake of muttering something I'd been thinking for at least an hour and a half.

"It's possible," I said, "that somewhere on God's green earth there's a more miserable place than this one."

Clayton barely moved his eyelids, then gave his night-crawler a sluggish twitch. "Lots of 'em," he mumbled.

He reeled in slowly, checked the crawler, and dropped its limp carcass back over the gunwales. Behind the water streaming down the lenses of his glasses his red face peered out like a goldfish in a Mason jar.

"Not the best day I ever fished," he finally said. "Then again, not the worst one neither." It was his favorite line, and I kicked myself for triggering the inevitable soliloquy. Clayton normally doesn't talk much, but if he gets started on tough days afield, he has the stamina of a musk ox. And not only on rotten weather. It's Clayton's *range* of firsthand experience on outdoor misery that sets him apart. From ungodly messes in the bottom of a tackle box to chimney fires or skunk scent on a pack of coonhounds, Clayton Stumpf is the measure by which outdoor suffering is judged.

Which brings me to the Hardship Test. To put it bluntly, what I finally got worn down enough to ask for, and what he finally came up with after we got home and he'd rummaged through a stack of old papers in his basement, is the list of questions below. Clayton says he ran across them a while back in one of the publications he subscribes to. The Test offers a gauge any hunter or fisherman can use to measure how his ability to handle misfortune stacks up against another man's. I'll pass it along here just in case you're curious about your own toleration index—what the quiz calls your "Manly Ability to Cope with Hardship Outdoors." According to Clayton, the M.A.C.H.O. Test is infallible as a barometer of suffering, no matter where you hunt or fish.

The M.A.C.H.O. Test

1. When a duck hunter's body temperature drops below 70 degrees, the condition is known as

   a. hypothermia.
   b. rigor mortis.
   c. The Big Chill.

2. When a duck hunter's body temperature drops below 70 degrees, the best revival tactic is to

   a. massage his pectorals.
   b. submerge him in the river.
   c. blow the feeding call and whisper "Don't move!"

3. When an ice fisherman is forced to answer a call of nature, the process is commonly known as

a. spelunking.
b. the Heimlich Maneuver.
c. finding the right fly.

4. Field Crisis Situation #1: During a heavy caddis hatch, you're casting to rising trout when you snag another fisherman in the earlobe. At this point, your best course of action is to

a. apologize for not using barbless hooks.
b. feed him slack line.
c. break off and shorten your backcasts.

5. Field Crisis Situation #2: In hurrying to get out on your favorite bass lake with a friend at sunset, you snap off his rod tip in the trunk. Do you

a. remind him of the time his dog chewed a hole in your rain gear?
b. offer him your car keys and any of the rods from the shelf back in your garage?
c. promise he can use your Ugly Stik as soon as you catch your limit?

6. Field Crisis Situation #3: A friend has just eaten an unidentified mushroom he mistakenly thought was a morel. Your most helpful words of reassurance are:

a. Of the many varieties of wild fungi, only three hundred and twenty-two are fatal.

b. All but forty-three of the poisonous variety can be identified through microscopic examination of the gills.

c. Statistics prove that anybody has a greater chance of dying from a heart attack than from eating a poisonous mushroom.

7. Many roots and shrubs long assumed to be inedible are now commonly regarded as gourmet table fare. This fact illustrates the widespread outdoor influence of

   a. Euell Gibbons.
   b. Fanny Farmer.
   c. Jim Beam.

8. On the average, chest waders begin to leak

   a. one week after purchase.
   b. two days after purchase.
   c. on initial contact with a lake or stream.

9. According to the Outdoorsman's Annual Mired Vehicle Index, the average hunter finds himself buried up to the axle between two and three times a year. Which of the following assertions most often precedes the immobilization?

   a. "We got through here last year."
   b. "No problem. This baby's got four-wheel drive."
   c. "See how shallow those deer tracks are? You can tell it's solid beneath that surface slop."

10. Which of the following scientific facts offers solace to the outdoorsman harassed by mosquitoes?

  a. Only the female bites.
  b. Mosquitoes bed down for up to six hours a day.
  c. Given a choice, mosquitoes prefer to feed on several other mammals, including lemmings, wombats, and wolverines.

11. Learning how to "read the woods" is becoming more and more essential to hunter success throughout North America. Along with buck scrapes and rubs, for example, areas of heaviest deer activity are usually marked by which of the following signs?

  a. "No Trespassing."
  b. "Keep Out!"
  c. "Private Property. Protected by Pit Bulls."

12. You know you've sat too long in your tree stand when

  a. a bush looks like a deer.
  b. a squirrel looks like a deer.
  c. a deer looks like a squirrel.

I've tried to convince Clayton that some of the questions don't have anything to do with hardship—for example the one that ends with Jim Beam. So far it hasn't done any good. He just grunts and says I obviously haven't spent enough time outdoors.

A Fly Fishing Primer

ACCORDING TO A RECENT ARTICLE IN MY NEWSPA-
per—one of those prediction lists of what will be "In" and "Out"
during the last decade of the twentieth century—only bagpipes
and aphrodisiacs are likely to be more "In" than fly fishermen.
If the soothsayers are right, the roll cast is about to rank with
the Rolls Royce and the Rolex as a status symbol.

It's hard to know what to make of this prospect of the
sport's becoming trendy. If you've always taken a perverse
satisfaction in the knowledge that it's tough to be hip in hip
boots, word that the Japanese are buying up grizzly necks like
chunks of Manhattan may inspire something less than evangeli-
cal glee.

Not that fly fishermen are selfish. On the contrary, for
every curmudgeon who hoards his favorite pocket water like

Fred C. Dobbs his stash of gold in the Sierra Madre, there are dozens who are generous to a fault. Most of the veterans I know are happy to show any newcomer how to weight an Irresistible, for example, or which cream dubbing to use for the butter fly. Some are even willing to divulge their favorite runs on the East River and the Cuyahoga.

No, it's not self-interest that raises doubts about the sport's going upscale. It's an impassioned commitment to keep Fly Fishing Tradition intact. There are certain proper ways of doing things if one wishes to consider himself a fly fisherman, ways long ago established as conventional. For the traditionalist the thought of suddenly being fashionable borders on sacrilege.

No angler, if he's honest, can tell you precisely where the Tradition originated. That fact acknowledged, it's fair to add that most traditionalists trace their lineage to Dame Juliana Berners's classic fifteenth-century *Treatyse of Fysshynge wyth an Angle*. The few dissenting voices echo as mere background notes. Let the novice never doubt it: where Fly Fishing Tradition is concerned, the legion of zealots who think of themselves as The AfterBerners are keepers of the flame.

The question of origins, of course, is properly the stuff not of trout streams but of taprooms. On the water, it's the Tradition alone that counts. What's important to any classicist is simply that the conventions be maintained, however one happens to learn them. And it's here, to reemphasize the point, that fly fishing's new In status is troubling. Trendiness is to the sport of Dame Juliana what a Teflon dome is to the pastoral world of Abner Doubleday.

In the face of such a threat, no one who considers himself a preservationist can afford to sit idly on the shoreline. Every veteran must do what he can. In that spirit, I recently took it upon myself to wade through the flood of recent books and articles targeted at fly fishing novices. What parts of the Tradition, I asked myself, are not being passed along to beginners? Where are the gaps?

Astoundingly, in the wash of pages devoted to such arcana as fringed *Leptophlebia* and the size-24 hen-hackle dun/brown spinner, I found a hole big enough to drive a truck through. The depressing fact is, nobody appears to be writing about the fly fishing *basics*—the proper way a beginner should do things, for example, when he first stands rod in hand in a stream.

The most glaring omission is proper attention to what my own hoary mentor liked to call the "Fundamental Four" of fly fishing: 1. Proper dressing of the fly; 2. Recognizing drag; 3. Wind knots; 4. Learning not to put rising fish down.

For the benefit of all newcomers (and any veterans who might need a refresher course), let's consider them one by one.

1. *Proper dressing of the fly:* Dressing your fly correctly before sending it off on its trip across the water is the touchstone of Traditional Angling, a rite as ancient as the sport itself. The roots lie firmly implanted in Dame Juliana, by all accounts an uncommonly stylish dresser who liked nothing better than fishing her angle while smartly clad in feathers and fur. The good Dame herself testifies to this fact in that section of the *Treatyse* which recounts the creation of her favorite fly, the Lady Caroline:

"A goodlie tyme hadde I fysshed, evere with woful fortune," she writes, "when the condicioune of my angle flye strooken sodenlye upon my eye. . . . Swiche a poore beggarlie thynge it was, who coulde wonder that the troutes treateth it nevere better than the lowlieste worme or dongemyte?"

Casting about for something more presentable, Dame

Juliana continues, she found her eye falling on the costly gown she was wearing, a "Yuletyde gyfte" from Lady Caroline Pembroke, Duchess of Kent. The epic passage that follows is arguably the most venerable in angling history, the birth of Fly Fishing Tradition itself:

'Why shulde not my angle flye lykewise go forth in semely attire?' sayeth I, pluckynge a golde silke threade from my collare. 'Wherefore shulde not it ryde as merrily bedecked in furre and fethere as the grettest governour upon the Thames?' Whereupon I dresseth out my poore angle flye in swiche finery as strooken the eyen wyth the moost likerous amaze and wonderment, and I proceedeth yet that eventyde to catche moore comelie troutes thanne ever I knewe lyveth in rennynge ryvere bifore.

Dame Juliana could not have left the beginning angler a more pointed object lesson: *Dress for success.* Silk, floss, the finest in lace and lingerie. Spare no expense in properly appareling your fly.

2. *Recognizing drag:* Perhaps because the "drag problem" is so basic—and so familiar to any veteran—it seems virtually to have been forgotten in recent instructional books aimed at fly fishing novices, much as a chef might explain how to make an omelette without noting that the eggs must first be taken from their shells. Such neglect ignores an angling truth that any experienced mentor will tell you is axiomatic: most beginners fail utterly to recognize the problems involved with drag.

Why they fail should be clear to anyone who has even a rudimentary grasp of the skill we have just examined, since recognition goes hand in glove with knowing how properly to dress the fly.

There's no difficulty, of course, with flies of the feminine gender: the Yellow Sallies, the Pink Ladies, the Parmachene Belles. Any of them can be put on the water dressed in as much fur and feather as the angler has means to supply. Nor is the beginner likely to cause more than an occasional raised eyebrow however he chooses to deck out what we today, in a more enlightened age, have come to call the "gender-neutral" attractors: the Professors, Silver Doctors, Bumble Pups.

The problem lies entirely with flies that are unmistakably masculine, where even the slightest hint of drag will not only make any trout in the vicinity skittish but embarrass other fishermen as well. Let's be frank: trying to pretty up a Woolly Bugger is akin to putting red tights on a stevedore. As even the most liberal follower of Dame Juliana would tell you, it just isn't done.

And yet every year we see more and more novices who seem to think that anything one can stick on a fly, short of lipstick and earrings, is correct. Little wonder that "too damned much drag" is the chronic lament of so many angling mentors. Of all the threats to Fly Fishing Tradition, in fact, the recent popularity of transvestite flies may be cause for the greatest alarm.

3. *Wind knots:* Two basic facts should be emphasized throughout a beginner's instruction in lines and leaders: a. *A good wind knot is by far the toughest of all knots to tie;* b. It is also the most resistant to any unraveling—and thus the tightest, longest-lasting knot he'll have in his repertoire.

True, the aptly named "blood knot" will sometimes leave the beginner's fingers torn and bleeding. And even a basic barrel knot may prove tricky if he gets caught without so much as a small beer keg around. Yet on those sunny, windless days that are the bane of every fly fisherman's existence, it's the wind knot that's going to pose the knottiest knot problem he'll ever face.

The reason why will be gin clear to any angler who has ever made even a tentative effort to tie one: *The good wind knot must be tied with no hands.* This alone makes the task difficult even on that rare perfect day when one finds himself working into a stiff headwind. When one further considers the distances at which a dedicated knotter often finds himself performing—his leader and tippet some fifty feet *behind* him looping over shoreline brush— it's little short of astonishing that even crude wind knots get tied at all.

Yet if they're game enough to stay with it, most anglers eventually learn how to tie at least a couple an outing, a fact the dispirited novice can't hear often enough. Through years of working with my own youngsters, I've learned that nothing raises their flagging spirits like evidence of my own modest triumphs, usually in the form of old tippets saved from trips to the Henry's Fork and Bitterroot. At such times I only wish I had better examples to show them. Indeed, some anglers consider a well-tied "windy" the most elegant accomplishment the sport has to offer. The greatest wind-knotters, like the classic fly-casters and rod-builders, have earned international acclaim. Lives there the fisherman who doesn't stand in awe of Sparse Grey Hackle's famed "Neversink Triple," for example, with its trio of flawless double-tucks tied in 8X tippet at a distance of some sixty feet? Judging from the evidence of the following passage in her *Treatyse,* at such an achievement even Dame Juliana would have been amazed:

At evensonge wondrous fierce dide the wynde blowe acrosse the Ryvere Itchen, whiche moost gladsome maketh my herte. Yet alas, nevere was I able to knytteth togidre e'en the loathlieste wynde knotte, howsoever oft my angle lyne launcheth I forth. Nor could evere Bisshoppe Bullswynke. For whiche grace, atte leaste, thanked be Godde.

4. *Putting rising fish down:* Putting a trout down is widely recognized as the crudest gaffe committed by the inexperienced angler. Rare is the veteran who hasn't seen entire pools turn quiet and sullen in response. Fortunately, the error is also the easiest of the Fundamental Four to explain to any novice, since he too, like the trout, is so sensitive to any perceived putdown. Because fly fishing tends to attract the upwardly mobile—people who are themselves on the rise, open to any window of opportunity—most beginners are insecure enough to appreciate what a graceless line or thoughtless barb can do to a rising fish.

For these and other obvious reasons, putting fish down nearly always registers with the novice as the worst sort of angling snobbery. It doesn't take a very big man to make a ten-inch trout feel like hiding in a hole.

All too easy to ignore, if you're a beginner, these

four fundamentals. Yet God willing, the day will never come when a well-dressed fly is but a memory and only a few grizzled AfterBerners remember how to tie the wind knot.

The Last Opener

MY WIFE SHOT BOLT UPRIGHT IN THE BED, THEN
groaned and sank back on her pillow.

"What time is it?"

"A quarter to four." I fumbled to turn off the alarm clock.
It appeared I'd slept for at least three hours—minus the time
I'd spent going to the bathroom and checking the weather
outside.

"My god, it's the middle of the night," she moaned.
"You've got to be demented."

"Close," I said.

She gave another moan, low and muted. Then her breathing
got heavier, and I was sure she'd fallen back to sleep.

A couple of minutes later I heard her whisper, "What are
you going to do this year?"

The Opener. Once again, the annual dilemma. Stay home and circle the house like a cage-crazed lion, remembering the "Never again" of other Openers? Or blot out the memories and join the jostling Spring-fed mobs along the stream?

"I don't know," I finally muttered. "What do you think?"

She turned toward me in the moonlight, her dark hair spread across the pillow, then reached over and took my hand.

"Let's look at it objectively," she said. "Out there it's three hours until daylight. The temperature's about forty degrees. Cars full of other fishermen are already parked beside all your favorite pools along the highway. In here you can sleep five more hours in a king-sized bed with an electric blanket, then have coffee, pancakes, and eggs. Think about it. Is it really such a tough choice?"

"You're right."

She squeezed my hand and appeared to smile faintly in the darkness.

"I'm going trout fishing," I said. "Thanks. You've been a big help."

She made the same sound I'd heard the day I backed over our mailbox trying to fasten my safety belt.

"I'm serious," I added. "What you said about the cars along the highway helped a lot. It reminded me there are still a few places that the yahoos can't get to, places like the Snake Eyes on the upper Willow. There are only two good pools, but you've got to hike about three miles through a bog to reach them. It's not likely I'd run into anybody else that far up. Even on Opening Day."

"Just don't lose your keys like last year and call me up from some old bachelor's farmhouse," she said, pulling the blankets over her head. "And try not to swear so much when you get home."

When I reached the Willow Creek bridge at five, a dozen cars were already parked along the highway. Most were empty; a few had other fishermen huddled inside. Opening the trunk, I took off my shoes and began to climb into my waders. A car door closed, and I heard footsteps approaching from behind.

In the dim glow of the trunk light the guy looked to be about thirty, round-faced and short, with shaggy hair and a tattered blanket draped over his shoulders. For a second I thought he was going to hand me a passage of Scripture or ask if I had any loose change.

"How's it goin'?" he said, raising a sneakered foot and propping it on the bumper. It wasn't a blanket, I saw then, but some kind of gray serape that he wore.

"Not bad," I answered, suddenly feeling better than I ever had in the darkness before an Opener. The guy was obviously a worm-dunker, the kind with an outside range of two, maybe three hundred yards. A few of the others might have a mile or two in them, but it was a good bet there wasn't a one who had even heard of The Snake Eyes, let alone want to hike that far up through the bog. Belting my waders, I slipped into my vest and uncased my rod.

"Wally Holiday," the stranger said, extending his hand, "but most of the dudes I know call me Doc." He paused while we shook, waiting for me to say something, then carried on. "I'm always thinkin', you know, about goin' into medicine and stuff."

"That so?" I said.

"Yo. I read all the time, you know, at the Seven-Eleven when I'm workin'? You'd be surprised how it pays off."

"No kidding?"

"Take them scissors on your vest," he said. "They're what you call surgeon's scissors. The only guys that wear 'em are the dudes that fish with flies."

"Is that right?" I said.

"So you gotta be a fly fisherman."

He smiled at me like he'd just hit on a cure for influenza.

"You're right," I said. "Good guess."

"I'll bet you're a tie-flyer too."

He watched as I strung my rod, but said nothing more for almost a minute. Then he reached in his pocket and pulled out a small plastic bag with what looked, under the trunk light, like a large cockroach inside.

"See this?" he said. He edged closer and dropped his voice to a conspiratorial whisper. "Whaddaya think it is?"

"Some kind of bug," I said.

"Heavy duty. It's a Rio Grande cricket, is what it is. Got him from this trucker I know. Down in Texas? Last week he brought me up a coupla' dozen. This is the only one of the little dudes that didn't crap out."

"What's it for?" I said.

He looked around as if the CIA were on his tail, then tapped the bag knowingly with his finger.

"These things are killers on bass," he said. "So I figured, hey, why shouldn't your basic trout get the same good vibes that bass do?"

"Could be," I offered. "Too bad you've only got one."

"Damn straight. It's a bummer, man—you know what I'm sayin'? I lose this little dude, I gotta go back to worms." He looked a bit downcast for a second, contemplating the diminished possibilities. Then he brightened suddenly and pulled something off the headband he wore around his hair.

"'Course I could always try this," he said, dropping it in my hand. This one looked like a Rio Grande cricket with hoof-and-mouth disease.

"Tied it myself," he added. "You know, at one of those Fish and Boat Shows up in the Cities? Where they bring in all those big honcho tie-flyers to get you started and stuff?"

"Never seen one quite like it," I said, nodding and turning it over. "What's it called?"

"It's a Gold-ribbed Earhair," he answered, holding it up close to the trunk light. He squinted like a jeweler eyeing a diamond and not finding a single flaw.

"It's real famous Out East," he continued. "Like your Texaco Nymph or Gray-Hackler Yellow Body? You oughta get yourself one."

"You're probably right," I said. "But right now I've got to get moving. It's not long until daybreak and I'm heading upstream a few hundred yards."

"Hey, man, I hear ya' talkin'. Catch ya' later. I got some serious hook work to do myself."

I hiked the first mile on the well-worn trail, my spirits rising with each outflanked knot of fishermen already jockeying for casting room around the perimeter of the choicest pools. Pipes and cigarettes glowed like tiny warning fires through the darkness, and an occasional grunt or mumble drifted my way as I passed.

The trail petered out in the second mile, just as I'd remembered, the shoreline now heavily overgrown with willows. I broke my rod down to keep from snapping it, then pushed on through the faint predawn light. It had been fifteen minutes since I'd seen another fisherman. An owl hooted. A flock of ducks spooked a few feet in front of me and lifted off the creek.

"All right," I murmured to myself. *"All right!"*

Panting heavily, I reached the third-mile bog as the eastern sky showed its first faint tint of color. If I didn't stop to rest, I told myself, I'd hit the Snake Eyes in perfect first casting light. My waders sucked heavily in the muck, every step a flatulent antiphon to the wheezing in my chest.

Twenty minutes later I staggered out of the bog and hauled myself the last two hundred yards through a bed of fiddlehead ferns to the Snake Eyes, collapsing to my knees below the lower pool. My hands were shaking so badly it was a full minute before I could restring my rod.

Was it fatigue, or anticipation? Ahead of me the black water gleamed through the rising steam, a daybreak out of the Stone Age. Beneath the gun-metal surface, wild fish lurked that hadn't seen a fly since God knows when.

A hundred yards upstream, the second pool crouched below a limestone shelf, barely visible in the half-light.

I tied on a pheasant-tail nymph and slid softly into the frigid current, false casting as I eased ahead. From the ridgetop above came the faint whine of a laboring motor—a farmer up and at his spring plowing, primed to seed the good earth. I eyed the oily water ahead, itself shining like a fresh-turned furrow, and with trembling hands planted the weighted nymph a foot below an overhanging rock. The sudden twitch on the still-taut line came so hard I struck back in winter-rusty clumsiness, snapping the 5X tippet at the knot.

"Goddamn," I mumbled. "Goddamn right!"

Above me the tractor's whine grew louder—the farmer approaching the end of his field. Still absorbed with the trout's heft, I fumbled in my vest for a spool of tippet material, then bit off a two-foot strand and began to knot it on.

The piercing whine of the tractor suddenly registered as if it were coming from a few feet beyond my right ear. Startled,

I looked up and saw two dim beams of light flickering through the gloom above me, a vehicle of some kind switchbacking its way downhill through the woods. It turned broadside on the last switch to reveal the battered gray hulk of an ancient pickup. Then it turned again and headed straight toward me, rattling over the frosted earth.

It stopped under an oak tree a few feet away. A short, stoop-shouldered old man climbed out and scuttled earnestly toward me, carrying a bucket and a casting rod.

"Any'ting hittin' yet, hey?" he said, dropping the bucket beside the pool and pulling out a sack of cheese balls.

The Geezer.

I looked down at my still untied leader and figured I was about to die of a broken heart.

"How did you *do* that?" I mumbled. "How'd you get your pickup down here off the ridge?"

"Dat old loggin' road, hey," he said, nodding toward the woods. He freed a snelled hook from the cork handle of his rod and threaded on a cheese ball. "Openin' Day, a man can come down here and get away from all da aggravation. It's a little hard on da body, sure, but dat old truck can handle it. Ain't no sense walkin' where you can drive."

He tied on a lead sinker the size of a jawbreaker. Then he sat down on the bucket, drew back his arm, and shot the cheese upstream toward a submerged log. The heavy line yawed across the water like a clothesline sagging in the wind.

"Whattcha waitin' on?" he said, nodding toward the shore-line run above me. "Dem fish might be hungry, hey, but dey ain't gonna jump up on da bank after your hook."

We fished for about an hour as the sun climbed higher above the ridgetop. Neither one of us had a strike. The Geezer hadn't risen once from his bucket, but he was clearly starting to get a little twitchy. He'd switched to a nightcrawler and was worrying bigger and bigger chaws of tobacco back and forth in his mouth. I began to nurse the hope that soon he'd give up and vacate. If he pulled out soon enough, I told myself, the pool might even recover in time for a midmorning hatch.

"It's da goddamned water," he finally said, breaking a twenty-minute silence between us. "Dey never hit when da water's dis clear."

"Absolutely right," I added hastily, scarcely able to believe the sudden stroke of fortune. "Damn water's like gin. Only an idiot would try to fish it. What we need's a real gully-washer to muddy this creek up good." I shook my head in feigned disgust, then reeled in and switched to a Leadwing Coachman.

The Geezer got up slowly and propped his rod against the bucket. "I tink you maybe got sometin' dere, hey," he said. Then he shuffled up the bank to where a shallow spring fed in above the pool's headwaters. Buckling his overshoes, he proceeded to step in and root around like a hog in a potato patch. A thick cloud of dirty brown water spread across the creek.

"What in God's name are you doing?" I shouted. "You're going to spook every fish from here down to the bridge!"

"Get dat rod workin' hey!" he answered. "Dem little bastards are gonna start feedin'. How you ever gonna get da job done standin' around scratchin' your butt?" He was chugging up and down the spring now like a garden tiller gone haywire, shuffling his feet jerkily from side to side.

Disgustedly, I raised my rod and dropped a halfhearted cast next to a rock along the shoreline. The fly sank and drifted toward me, stripped line coiling at my knees. I picked up and cast again, just as fruitlessly, then splattered down two or three more in sullen insurrection. By then the Geezer had begun to wind down.

Puffing heavily, he plowed one last downstream furrow, then lurched into a bowlegged stagger out of the spring. He looked at me as if I'd just broken a bottle of his favorite schnapps.

"Dat's da 'ting wit' dem flies, hey," he wheezed. "Dey never work when ya got good water. Get down to da nut cuttin', and dere wort'less as tits on a boar." He picked up his rod disgustedly and began to reel in, then suddenly set the hook hard and scrambled backward.

"I got one, hey!" he shouted. "By Got, I got a good one on now for sure!" His rod was bent almost double, the heavy line throbbing in the current. It did look as if in fact by some fluke he was hooked up with a good-sized fish.

I think the next thing he yelled was to get a landing net out of the back of his pickup. I'm not sure, because when he said it I was already halfway to the upper pool.

The sun had spread over its shadowy depths a few minutes earlier, and I stood for a moment simply staring at the quiet water above me. A small fish surfaced in a splashy rise as I watched.

Quickly tying on a Quill Gordon, I cast to it and was immediately fast to the season's first trout, a fat, scrappy ten-incher. I released it and dried the fly as other fish began to rise sporadically upstream.

I was landing my third small brown when I heard the cough. Someone was trotting up the shoreline behind me. Spell snapped like a frazzled tippet, I froze, fish in hand.

"Little dude?" chirped the intruder. "The little dudes've started raising?"

It was Doc Holiday. If I'd had a sidearm, you'd know the Snake Eyes the same way you know the O.K. Corral.

Instead, my hand lifted off the trout, and I turned to give

him the most menacing glower in my arsenal. It was clear he was taken aback.

"Hey," he said, hands upraised, the serape sliding off his shoulders. "Maybe he wasn't that little. He was prob'ly a lot bigger than I thought."

"I'm *fishing* here!" I said, biting down hard on the second syllable.

A smile gradually returned to his round face, and he hopped a couple of eager steps forward. "You sure are, man," he said. "Me and that old guy down below have both been watchin' you. You been fishin' the livin' crap out o' this hole."

"He sent you up here?"

"The old guy?" he said. "Nah."

He raised his spinning rod and drew it back over his shoulder. I couldn't tell if it was the Rio Grande cricket or the Earhair that swung like a fuzzy dirtball from the tip.

"Good old dude, though," he went on. "He told me this hole'd be a whole lot clearer than the other one."

The rod shot forward and coils of monofilament spun fifty feet up the creek.

"Down there somethin' real weird happened to the water. You oughta go down and check it out, man. It's all filled up with crud."